Ready, Set, Go!

Cookbook

125 Easy Meals to Get You Started

About CWeight Watchers

Weight Watchers International, Inc., is the world's leading provider of weight-management services, operating globally through a network of company-owned and franchise operations. Weight Watchers holds nearly 50,000 weekly meetings worldwide, at which members receive group support and education about healthful eating patterns, behavior modification, and physical activity. Weight-loss and weight-management results vary by individual. We recommend that you attend Weight Watchers meetings to benefit from the supportive environment you find there and follow the comprehensive Weight Watchers program, which includes a food plan, an activity plan, and a behavioral component. In addition, Weight Watchers offers a wide range of products, publications, and programs for people interested in weight loss and weight control. For the Weight Watchers meeting nearest you, call **1-800-651-6000**. For information about bringing Weight Watchers to your workplace, call **1-800-8AT-WORK**. Also visit us at our Web site, **WeightWatchers.com**, and look for *Weight Watchers Magazine* at your newsstand or in your meeting room.

Feta-Stuffed Chicken Breasts, page 99

Weight Watchers Publishing Group

Editorial Director NANCY GAGLIARDI

Creative Director ED MELNITSKY

Production Manager ALAN BIEDERMAN

Photo Editor DEBORAH HARDT

Managing Editor SARAH WHARTON

Editorial Assistant KATERINA GKIONIS

Food Editor EILEEN RUNYAN

Editor DEBORAH MINTCHEFF

Nutrition Consultant PATTY SANTELLI

Photographer ANTONIS ACHILLEOS

Food Stylist JAMIE KIMM

Prop Stylist PAIGE HICKS

Cover Designer DANIELA HRITCU

Art Director PAULINE NEUWIRTH

About Our Recipes

While losing weight isn't only about what you eat, Weight Watchers realizes the critical role it plays in your success and overall good health. That's why our philosophy is to offer great-tasting, easy recipes that are nutritious as well as delicious. We make every attempt to use wholesome ingredients and to ensure that our recipes fall within the recommendations of the U.S. Dietary Guidelines for Americans for a diet that promotes health and reduces the risk for disease. If you have special dietary needs, consult with your health-care professional for advice on a diet that is best for you and how to adapt these recipes to meet your specific nutritional needs.

To achieve these good-health goals and get the maximum satisfaction from the foods you eat, we suggest you keep the following information in mind while preparing our recipes:

The *PointsPlus*® Program and Good Nutrition

► Recipes in this book have been developed for Weight Watchers members who are following the *PointsPlus* program. *PointsPlus* values are given for each recipe. They're assigned based on the amount of protein (grams), carbohydrates (grams), fat (grams), and fiber (grams), contained in a single serving of a recipe.

► Recipes include approximate nutritional information; they are analyzed for Calories (Cal), Total Fat, Saturated Fat (Sat Fat), Trans Fat, Cholesterol (Chol), Sodium (Sod), Total Carbohydrates (Total Carb), Total Sugar, Dietary Fiber (Fib), Protein (Prot), and Calcium (Calc). The nutritional values are calculated by registered dietitians, using nutrition analysis software.

► Substitutions made to the ingredients will alter the per-serving nutritional information and may affect the *PointsPlus* value.

► Our recipes meet Weight Watchers Good Health Guidelines for eating lean proteins and fiber-rich whole grains, and having at least five servings of vegetables and fruits and two servings of low-fat or fat-free dairy products a day, while limiting your intake of saturated fat, sugar, and sodium.

▸ Health agencies recommend an intake of no more than 2,300 mg sodium daily. To stay in line with these recommendations we keep sodium levels in our recipes reasonably low; to boost flavor, we often include fresh herbs or a squeeze of citrus instead of salt. If you don't have to restrict your sodium, feel free to add a touch more salt as desired.

▸ In the recipes a green triangle (▲) indicates Weight Watchers Power Foods.

▸ ▲ Healthy Extra suggestions have a *PointsPlus* value of **0** unless otherwise stated.

▸ Recipes that work with the Simply Filling technique are listed on page 15. Find more details about this technique at your meeting.

▸ For more about the science behind lasting weight loss and more, please visit **WeightWatchers.com/science.**

PointsPlus value not what you expected?

▸ You might expect some of the *PointsPlus* values in this book to be lower when some of the foods they're made from, such as fruits and vegetables, have no *PointsPlus* values. Fruit and most veggies have no *PointsPlus* values when served as a snack or part of a meal, like a cup of berries with a sandwich. But if these foods are part of a recipe, their fiber and nutrient content are incorporated into the recipe calculations. These nutrients can affect the *PointsPlus* values.

▸ Alcohol is included in our *PointsPlus* calculations. Because alcohol information is generally not included on nutrition labels, it's not an option to include when using the hand calculator or the online calculator. But since we incorporate alcohol information from our nutritionists you might notice discrepancies between the *PointsPlus* values you see in our recipes, and the values you get using the calculator. The *PointsPlus* values listed for our recipes are the most accurate values.

Shopping for Ingredients

As you learn to eat healthier and add more Power Foods to your meals, remember these tips for choosing foods wisely:

▸ Purchase lean meats and poultry, and trim them of all visible fat before cooking. When poultry is cooked with the skin on, we recommend removing the skin before eating. Nutritional information for recipes that include meat, poultry, and fish is based on cooked, skinless boneless portions (unless otherwise stated), with the fat trimmed.

▶ Whenever possible, our recipes call for seafood that is sustainable and deemed the most healthful for human consumption so that your choice of seafood is not only good for the oceans but also good for you. For more information about the best seafood choices and to download a pocket guide, go to **environmentaldefensefund.org** or **montereybayaquarium.org**. For information about mercury and seafood go to **weightwatchers.com**.

▶ For best flavor, maximum nutrient content, and the lowest prices, buy fresh, local produce, such as vegetables, leafy greens, and fruits in season. Rinse them thoroughly before using and keep a supply of cut-up vegetables and fruits in your refrigerator for convenient, healthy snacks.

▶ Explore your market for whole-grain products such as whole wheat and whole-grain breads and pastas, brown rice, bulgur, barley, cornmeal, whole-wheat couscous, oats, and quinoa to enjoy with your meals.

Preparation and Measuring

▶ Take a couple of minutes to read through the ingredients and directions before you start to prepare a recipe. This will prevent you from discovering midway through that you don't have an important ingredient or that a recipe requires several hours of marinating. And it's also a good idea to assemble all ingredients and utensils within easy reach before you begin a recipe.

▶ The success of any recipe depends on accurate weighing and measuring. The effectiveness of the Weight Watchers program and the accuracy of the nutritional analysis depend on correct measuring as well. Use the following techniques:

- Weigh food such as meat, poultry, and fish on a food scale.
- To measure liquids, use a standard glass or plastic measuring cup placed on a level surface. For amounts less than ¼ cup, use standard measuring spoons.
- To measure dry ingredients, use metal or plastic measuring cups that come in ¼-, ⅓-, ½-, and 1-cup sizes. Fill the appropriate cup and level it with the flat edge of a knife or spatula. For amounts less than ¼ cup, use standard measuring spoons.

French-Style Roast Chicken,
page 88

Contents

Escarole Salad Pizza,
page 154

Recipes by *PointsPlus* value

PointsPlus value: 5

Asian Chicken Salad, 53

Asparagus-Chicken Salad with Lemon Dressing, 51

Beef and Parmesan Bruschetta, 130

Crispiest Oven-Fried Chicken, 92

Grilled Chicken and Asparagus with Capers and Basil, 94

Grilled Nectarines with Raspberry Sorbet and Berries, 164

Hearty Beef-Bulgur Loaf, 79

Lamb, Bacon, and Bean Chili, 86

Middle Eastern–Style Chicken Sandwiches, 38

North African Meatball Stew, 80

Rosemary Chicken with Cherry Tomato Sauce, 93

Szechuan Turkey, 172

Tex Mex–Style Frittata, 25

Turkey and Green Bean Salad with Yogurt-Mint Dressing, 54

Turkey-Vegetable Noodle Bowl, 187

Waffle and Berry Breakfast Parfaits, 35

PointsPlus value: 6

Brown Sugar Porridge, 33

Chinese-Style Barbecued Chicken, 100

Curried Bean-Walnut Burgers, 67

Easy Salmon Cakes with Tartar Sauce, 64

Egg, Tomato, and Avocado Tostadas, 22

Kung Pao Chicken, 171

Lemony Arctic Char with Black Bean Salad, 104

Oven-Roasted Vegetable Burritos, 45

Pork Piccata, 182

Pork with Rice Noodles and Vegetables, 61

Salmon and Vegetable Teriyaki, 189

Shepherd's Pie, 87

Tex-Mex Chef's Salad, 193

Thai Steak Skewers, 197

Tuna with Fennel, Orange, and Olive Salad, 109

Turkey Chili with Black Beans, 196

Turkey, Roasted Pepper, and Ricotta Panini, 43

Turkey Sausages with Warm Potato Salad, 102

Two Grain–Stuffed Peppers, 120

Vegetable Dal, 181

PointsPlus value: 7

Apple-Walnut "Stuffed" Pancakes, 32

Asparagus and Shrimp Stir-Fry, 114

Bean Salad–Topped Pita Wedges, 59

Breakfast Strata, 28

Chicken and Mushroom Pizza, 48

Chunky Fish Chowder, 71

Cod with Puttanesca Sauce, 107

Easy Chimichangas, 194

Ginger Shrimp and Vegetables, 201

Greek Orzo and Beef Casserole, 174

Grilled Tuna Niçoise Salad, 55

Ham, Brown Rice, and Pea Salad, 50

Mushroom and Spinach–Stuffed Trout, 110

Niçoise-Style Tuna Sandwiches, 41

Pork Lo Mein, 169

Risotto with Sausage and Greens, 183

Scallop and Bell Pepper Stir-Fry, 192

Shrimp and Chicken Jambalaya, 112

Two-Grain Pancakes, 30

Vegetable-Cheese Quesadillas, 46

Vegetarian Moussaka, 122

PointsPlus value: 8

Baked Cinnamon-Vanilla French Toast, 29

Broiled Lamb Kebabs with Spinach-Lentil Salad, 85

Chicken Thighs with Spinach and Mushrooms, 97

Classic Macaroni Salad, 58

**Grilled Nectarines with Raspberry
Sorbet and Berries, page 164**

Recipes that work with the Simply Filling technique

1

Breakfast

Overstuffed Western Omelette

Overstuffed Western Omelette

Per Serving

LEVEL Basic
PREP 10 min
COOK 10 min
SERVES 2

▲ ½ **cup diced green bell pepper**

▲ ½ **cup diced red bell pepper**

▲ 2 **scallions, thinly sliced**

▲ ¼ **pound piece low-sodium fat-free Virginia ham, diced**

⅛ **teaspoon black pepper**

▲ 1 **cup fat-free egg substitute**

1. Lightly spray medium nonstick skillet with nonstick spray and set over medium heat. Add green and red bell peppers, scallions, ham, and black pepper; cook, stirring, until vegetables are softened, about 5 minutes.

2. Pour in egg substitute and cook until almost set, about 3 minutes, gently lifting edge of eggs with silicone spatula to allow uncooked portion of egg to run underneath. Fold omelette in half and cook until set, about 2 minutes longer. Cut in half and place one half on each of 2 plates.

PER SERVING (½ OF OMELETTE): 266 grams, 144 Cal, 2 g Total Fat, 1 g Sat Fat, 0 g Trans Fat, 25 mg Chol, 674 mg Sod, 9 g Total Carb, 5 g Total Sugar, 2 g Fib, 22 g Prot, 56 mg Calc.

 FYI Popular in diners across America, this ever-popular omelette is known as a **Denver omelette** in some regions.

French Country-Style Omelette

LEVEL Basic
PREP 5 min
COOK 10 min
SERVES 2

▲ 1 **small zucchini, thinly sliced**

▲ 1 **cup thinly sliced white mushrooms**

▲ 1 **tomato, seeded and chopped**

½ **teaspoon dried thyme**

⅛ **teaspoon salt**

⅛ **teaspoon black pepper**

▲ 1 **cup fat-free egg substitute**

1 **tablespoon low-fat (1%) milk**

4 **tablespoons crumbled reduced-fat soft goat cheese**

2 **tablespoons snipped fresh chives**

1. Lightly spray medium nonstick skillet with nonstick spray and set over medium heat. Add zucchini, mushrooms, tomato, thyme, salt, and pepper; cook, stirring, until vegetables are softened, about 3 minutes. Transfer to plate.

2. Beat together egg substitute and milk in 2-cup glass measure.

3. Wipe skillet clean. Spray skillet with nonstick spray and set over medium heat. Pour in half of egg mixture and cook until almost set, about 3 minutes, gently lifting edge of eggs with silicone spatula to allow uncooked portion of egg to run underneath. Spoon half of vegetable mixture over half of omelette. Top with 2 tablespoons of goat cheese and 1 tablespoon of chives. Fold unfilled portion of omelette over filling. Slide omelette onto plate and keep warm. Repeat with remaining egg mixture, vegetable mixture, cheese, and chives to make another omelette.

PER SERVING (1 OMELETTE): 314 grams, 119 Cal, 2 g Total Fat, 1 g Sat Fat, 0 g Trans Fat, 3 mg Chol, 470 mg Sod, 10 g Total Carb, 6 g Total Sugar, 2 g Fib, 16 g Prot, 78 mg Calc.

▲ **HEALTHY EXTRA** Double the amount of mushrooms for an even more delicious omelette.

Vitamin & Mineral Supplements

▶ **Check the label.** Choose a supplement that contains no more than 100 percent of the daily recommendation for vitamins and minerals. And check the expiration date—it should be at least six months from the date of purchase.

▶ **Look for the purity symbol.** If a supplement shows the verification logo of the United States Pharmacopeia (USP), the USP confirms that the product contains the ingredients and the amount of each ingredient listed on the label, is free of harmful contaminants, and was manufactured according to safe and sanitary procedures.

▶ **Take it with a meal.** It's best to swallow a supplement during or after a meal because food boosts your body's ability to absorb key nutrients. If you can't stand swallowing pills, try chewable multivitamins.

Egg, Tomato, and Avocado Tostadas

6 PointsPlus value
Per Serving

LEVEL Basic
PREP 15 min
BROIL/COOK 15 min
SERVES 4

4   (6-inch) corn tortillas
▲ 1   large tomato, chopped
½   Hass avocado, pitted, peeled, and diced
▲ 2   scallions, thinly sliced
¼   cup chopped fresh cilantro
1   tablespoon lime juice
1   teaspoon olive oil
⅛   teaspoon black pepper
▲ 1   (7-ounce) baking potato, cooked, peeled, and diced
▲ 1   (2-ounce) piece low-sodium fat-free ham, chopped
▲ 2   cups fat-free egg substitute
▲ ¼   cup fat-free tomatillo salsa

1. Preheat broiler.

2. Place tortillas, in one layer, on rack of broiler pan. Broil 4 inches from heat until golden, about 2 minutes per side.

3. Meanwhile, mix together tomato, avocado, scallions, cilantro, lime juice, oil, and pepper in medium bowl.

4. Spray medium nonstick skillet with nonstick spray and set over medium heat. Add potato and ham; cook, stirring occasionally, until lightly browned, about 5 minutes. Transfer to small bowl; keep warm.

5. Wipe skillet clean. Spray with nonstick spray and set over medium heat. Add egg substitute and cook until eggs are set, about 4 minutes, pushing egg mixture toward center of skillet to form large, soft curds. Divide egg mixture evenly among tortillas, then top evenly with potato mixture, tomato mixture, and salsa.

PER SERVING (1 TOSTADA): 292 grams, 239 Cal, 6 g Total Fat, 1 g Sat Fat, 0 g Trans Fat, 8 mg Chol, 542 mg Sod, 28 g Total Carb, 5 g Total Sugar, 5 g Fib, 19 g Prot, 97 mg Calc.

FYI **Tostadas** are usually made with fried corn tortillas. Broiling the tortillas keeps the fat way down while making them crispy.

Egg, Tomato, and Avocado Tostadas

Scrambled Eggs with Peppers and Onion

4 PointsPlus value
Per Serving

LEVEL Basic
PREP 10 min
COOK 15 min
SERVES 4

▲ **2 cups fat-free egg substitute**

½ **teaspoon dried oregano**

¼ **teaspoon salt**

¼ **teaspoon black pepper**

2 **teaspoons olive oil**

▲ **1 red bell pepper, chopped**

▲ **2 Italian frying peppers, chopped**

▲ **½ small red onion, chopped**

▲ **2 cooked small potatoes, cut into small dice**

1. Whisk together egg substitute, oregano, salt, and black pepper in medium bowl.

2. Heat oil in large nonstick skillet over medium heat. Add bell pepper, frying peppers, and onion; cook, stirring, until softened, about 8 minutes. Stir in potatoes and cook, stirring, until heated through, about 3 minutes. Transfer to plate.

3. Wipe skillet clean. Spray with nonstick spray and set over medium heat. Add egg mixture and cook until eggs begin to set, about 1 ½ minutes, pushing egg mixture toward center of skillet to form large soft curds. Stir in vegetable mixture and cook until heated through, about 2 minutes longer.

PER SERVING (¼ OF EGGS): 251 grams, 161 Cal, 3 g Total Fat, 0 g Sat Fat, 0 g Trans Fat, 0 mg Chol, 403 mg Sod, 20 g Total Carb, 5 g Total Sugar, 2 g Fib, 14 g Prot, 58 mg Calc.

▲ **HEALTHY EXTRA** Serve a slice of fat-free Swiss cheese alongside each portion of eggs. A ¾-ounce slice of fat-free cheese with each serving will increase the *PointsPlus* value by *1*.

Tex Mex–Style Frittata

5
PointsPlus®
value
Per Serving

LEVEL Basic

PREP 10 min

COOK 15 min

SERVES 4

▲ **4   large eggs**

▲ **4   large egg whites**

▲ **¼   cup fat-free milk**

  2   teaspoons chili powder

  ¼   teaspoon salt

▲ **1   cup frozen corn kernels, thawed**

▲ **1   (4 ½-ounce) can chopped mild green chiles, drained**

▲ **12   cherry tomatoes, halved**

  ½   cup shredded reduced-fat sharp Cheddar cheese

1. Beat eggs, egg whites, milk, chili powder, and salt in large bowl. Stir in corn and chiles.

2. Spray medium nonstick skillet with nonstick spray and set over medium heat. Add egg mixture; top evenly with tomatoes. Cover and cook until eggs are almost set, about 10 minutes. Sprinkle with Cheddar; cook, covered until eggs are set and cheese is melted, about 5 minutes longer. Cut frittata into 4 wedges. Serve hot, warm, or at room temperature.

PER SERVING (1 WEDGE): 227 grams, 200 Cal, 9 g Total Fat, 4 g Sat Fat, 0 g Trans Fat, 223 mg Chol, 308 mg Sod, 17 g Total Carb, 5 g Total Sugar, 3 g Fib, 17 g Prot, 153 mg Calc.

▲ **HEALTHY EXTRA** Serve toasted slices of reduced-calorie bread alongside each portion of frittata (2 slices of reduced-calorie bread with each serving will increase the *PointsPlus* value by *3*).

On-The-Go Breakfast Burrito

On-The-Go Breakfast Burrito

LEVEL Basic
PREP 10 min
COOK 5 min
SERVES 1

1   **teaspoon canola oil**

▲ ½   **cup fat-free egg substitute**

⅛   **teaspoon black pepper**

1   **(7-inch) reduced-fat whole wheat tortilla, warmed**

3   **tablespoons shredded reduced-fat pepper Jack cheese**

▲ 1   **small tomato, chopped**

▲ 1   **large scallion, thinly sliced**

▲ 2   **tablespoons fat-free salsa**

1. Heat oil in medium nonstick skillet over medium heat.

2. Whisk together egg substitute and pepper in small bowl until frothy. Pour into skillet and cook, stirring, until just set, about 2 minutes.

3. Spoon eggs onto warm tortilla. Top with pepper Jack, tomato, scallion, and salsa. Roll tortilla up to enclose filling.

PER SERVING (1 BURRITO): 331 grams, 301 Cal, 11 g Total Fat, 3 g Sat Fat, 0 g Trans Fat, 15 mg Chol, 748 mg Sod, 32 g Total Carb, 10 g Total Sugar, 3 g Fib, 22 g Prot, 312 mg Calc.

▲ **HEALTHY EXTRA** This burrito makes a perfect brown bag breakfast. Wrap it tightly in foil to keep it nice and warm. And be sure to pack along a peeled and sectioned orange for a refreshing finish.

Breakfast Strata

7
PointsPlus
value
Per Serving

LEVEL Basic

PREP 20 min

COOK/BAKE 1 hr 10 min

SERVES 8

1   **teaspoon canola oil**

▲ 2   **onions, chopped**

8   **slices turkey bacon, cut into ½-inch pieces**

▲ 1   **cup grape tomatoes, halved**

▲ 2   **cups fat-free milk**

▲ 3   **large eggs**

▲ 3   **large egg whites**

½   **teaspoon dried oregano**

▲ 16   **slices reduced-calorie whole wheat bread, cut into ½-inch cubes**

1   **cup shredded reduced-fat Swiss cheese**

1. Spray 9 x 13-inch baking dish with nonstick spray.

2. Heat oil in large nonstick skillet set over medium heat. Add onions and bacon; cook, stirring, until onions are softened and bacon is crisp cooked, about 8 minutes. Remove skillet from heat; stir in tomatoes.

3. Whisk together milk, eggs, egg whites, and oregano in medium bowl. Spread half of bread cubes in prepared baking dish; top with half of onion mixture and half of Swiss. Pour half of milk mixture evenly over cheese. Repeat to make one more layer. Cover baking dish with plastic wrap and refrigerate at least 1 hour or up to overnight.

4. Preheat oven to 350°F.

5. Remove plastic wrap from strata. Bake until puffed, golden, and knife inserted into center comes out clean, about 1 hour. Let stand 5 minutes before cutting into 8 portions.

PER SERVING (⅛ OF STRATA): 223 grams, 257 Cal, 10 g Total Fat, 4 g Sat Fat, 0 g Trans Fat, 103 mg Chol, 518 mg Sod, 29 g Total Carb, 8 g Total Sugar, 7 g Fib, 17 g Prot, 286 mg Calc.

FYI A strata is an ideal company dish, as it can be prepared way ahead. Refrigerating it overnight gives the bread enough time to absorb all of the great flavors.

Baked Cinnamon-Vanilla French Toast

8 PointsPlus® value

Per Serving

LEVEL Basic
PREP 15 min
BAKE 25 min
SERVES 6

2   cups low-fat (1%) milk
▲ 3   large eggs
▲ 2   large egg whites
2   teaspoons sugar
2   teaspoons vanilla extract
1   teaspoon ground cinnamon
1   (1-pound) loaf challah or other egg bread, cut into 12 slices
6   teaspoons pure maple syrup

1. Preheat oven to 425°F. Spray two jelly-roll pans with nonstick spray.

2. Whisk together milk, eggs, egg whites, sugar, vanilla, and cinnamon in pie plate or large shallow bowl.

3. Dip bread, one slice at a time, into milk mixture, turning to coat well on each side. Transfer to prepared pans.

4. Bake French toast until slightly puffed and browned, about 12 minutes per side. Serve with maple syrup.

PER SERVING (2 SLICES FRENCH TOAST AND 1 TEASPOON MAPLE SYRUP): 202 grams, 318 Cal, 8 g Total Fat, 3 g Sat Fat, 0 g Trans Fat, 148 mg Chol, 464 mg Sod, 46 g Total Carb, 11 g Total Sugar, 2 g Fib, 14 g Prot, 188 mg Calc.

▲ **HEALTHY EXTRA** Serve this enticing buttery, vanilla-scented French toast with a generous bowl of fresh berries.

Two-Grain Pancakes

LEVEL Basic

PREP 15 min

COOK 20 min

SERVES 4

▲ 1   **large egg**

▲ 1   **large egg white**

▲ 1   **cup plain fat-free yogurt**

▲ ½   **cup unsweetened applesauce**

1   **tablespoon canola oil**

1   **tablespoon honey**

¾   **cup white whole wheat flour**

½   **cup buckwheat flour**

2   **teaspoons baking powder**

¼   **teaspoon salt**

8   **teaspoons pure maple syrup**

1. Whisk together egg, egg white, yogurt, applesauce, oil, and honey in small bowl. Whisk together white whole wheat flour, buckwheat flour, baking powder, and salt in large bowl. Add yogurt mixture to flour mixture, stirring just until flour mixture is moistened.

2. Spray large nonstick griddle or skillet with nonstick spray and set over medium heat. Pour ¼ cupfuls of batter onto griddle. Cook until bubbles appear and edges of pancakes look dry, about 3 minutes. Turn pancakes over and cook until golden brown on second side, about 3 minutes longer. Transfer to platter and keep warm. Repeat with remaining batter, making total of 12 pancakes.

PER SERVING (3 PANCAKES AND 2 TEASPOONS MAPLE SYRUP): 172 grams, 275 Cal, 6 g Total Fat, 1 g Sat Fat, 0 g Trans Fat, 54 mg Chol, 401 mg Sod, 50 g Total Carb, 20 g Total Sugar, 5 g Fib, 10 g Prot, 132 mg Calc.

▲ **HEALTHY EXTRA** Add a handful of fresh blueberries and strawberries to each serving of pancakes.

Two-Grain Pancakes

Apple-Walnut "Stuffed" Pancakes

7 PointsPlus value
Per Servin

LEVEL Basic
PREP 15 min
COOK 20 min
SERVES 6

1   teaspoon butter
▲ 1   **large apple, peeled, cored, and chopped**
3   teaspoons sugar
½   **teaspoon ground cinnamon**
⅛   **teaspoon ground nutmeg**
2   **cups reduced-fat all-purpose baking mix**
2   **tablespoons finely chopped walnuts**
1 ¼ cups low-fat (1%) milk
▲ 1   **large egg, lightly beaten**

1. Melt butter in large nonstick skillet over medium heat. Add apple, 1 teaspoon of sugar, the cinnamon, and nutmeg. Cook, stirring, until apple is tender, about 4 minutes. Transfer apple mixture to bowl.

2. Stir together baking mix, walnuts, milk, egg, and remaining 2 teaspoons sugar in large bowl until blended.

3. Spray nonstick griddle or skillet with nonstick spray and set over medium heat. Pour scant ¼ cupfuls of batter onto griddle. Immediately spoon 1 tablespoon of apple mixture onto each pancake. Cook until bubbles appear and edges of pancakes look dry, about 3 minutes. Turn pancakes over and cook until golden brown on second side, about 3 minutes longer. Transfer to platter and keep warm. Repeat with remaining batter, making total of 12 pancakes.

PER SERVING (2 PANCAKES): 143 grams, 237 Cal, 7 g Total Fat, 2 g Sat Fat, 0 g Trans Fat, 39 mg Chol, 501 mg Sod, 39 g Total Carb, 11 g Total Sugar, 1 g Fib, 6 g Prot, 113 mg Calc.

 FYI Use a **Golden Delicious apple** if you prefer more sweetness and a **Granny Smith apple** if a tart-sweet flavor is more to your liking.

Brown Sugar Porridge

6 PointsPlus© value

Per Serving

LEVEL Basic

PREP 15 min

COOK 20 min

SERVES 6

1 ½ **cups water**

▲ 1 **cup whole wheat couscous**

¼ **teaspoon salt**

3 **cups low-fat (1%) milk**

3 **tablespoons brown sugar**

▲ ¼ **cup fat-free egg substitute**

¼ **cup wheat germ**

1 ½ **teaspoons vanilla extract**

1. Bring water to boil in large heavy saucepan over high heat. Stir in couscous and salt. Reduce heat and simmer until water is absorbed, about 2 minutes. Remove saucepan from heat and fluff couscous with fork. Cover and let stand 5 minutes.

2. Stir milk and brown sugar into couscous. Bring to boil over medium-high heat, whisking frequently to break up lumps. Reduce heat to medium-low and cook, stirring frequently, until mixture is slightly thickened, about 5 minutes. Remove saucepan from heat.

3. Whisk together ½ cup of couscous mixture and the egg substitute in small bowl. Return mixture to saucepan; cook over low heat, stirring, until porridge is thick and creamy, about 5 minutes longer. Stir in wheat germ and vanilla.

PER SERVING (GENEROUS ¾ CUP PORRIDGE):
241 grams, 242 Cal, 3 g Total Fat, 1 g Sat Fat,
0 g Trans Fat, 5 mg Chol, 185 mg Sod, 45 g Total Carb,
13 g Total Sugar, 5 g Fib, 12 g Prot, 176 mg Calc.

▲ **HEALTHY EXTRA** Top each serving of this good-for-you porridge with sliced strawberries or diced apple.

Milk, Cheese & Yogurt

▶ **Prepare hot cereal a different way.** Instead of using water, as the package directions suggest, cook hot cereal with fat-free milk. It will give your oatmeal or farina (Cream of Wheat) a creamier than usual texture and will start your day with a healthy serving of calcium.

▶ **Count your coffee.** If you aren't crazy about milk, remember that the milk you put in your coffee counts toward your daily intake. So treat yourself to an afternoon pick-me-up of fat-free café au lait, latte, or cappuccino and know you'll be doing your health a favor along with your taste buds.

▶ **Add cheese and milk to egg dishes.** Cooking up a soufflé, strata, quiche, or frittata can be a delicious way to incorporate a dairy serving into your daily menu because these dishes typically include milk and cheese. What's more, they are versatile—you can serve one for brunch, lunch, or dinner.

Waffle and Berry Breakfast Parfaits

LEVEL Basic

PREP 15 min

COOK None

SERVES 6

▲ **2 (6-ounce) containers raspberries**

1 tablespoon granulated sugar

Grated zest of ½ orange

▲ **1 (15-ounce) container fat-free ricotta cheese**

3 tablespoons confectioners' sugar

½ teaspoon ground cinnamon

⅛ teaspoon ground nutmeg

6 frozen low-fat waffles, toasted and cut into pieces

1. Toss together raspberries, granulated sugar, and orange zest in medium bowl. Let stand 5 minutes.

2. Combine ricotta, confectioners' sugar, cinnamon, and nutmeg in food processor and puree. Alternately layer ricotta mixture, waffle pieces, and berry mixture in 6 parfait glasses or goblets, ending with berries.

PER SERVING (1 PARFAIT): 169 grams, 189 Cal, 2 g Total Fat, 2 g Sat Fat, 0 g Trans Fat, 19 mg Chol, 224 mg Sod, 34 g Total Carb, 12 g Total Sugar, 5 g Fib, 9 g Prot, 180 mg Calc.

▲ **HEALTHY EXTRA** Stir 1 cup of diced mango or papaya into the raspberry mixture.

2

Lunch

Middle Eastern–Style Chicken Sandwiches

5
PointsPlus
value

Per Servi

LEVEL Basic
PREP 20 min
COOK None
SERVES 4

▲ ¾ **cup plain fat-free yogurt**

▲ ½ **cup shredded cucumber, squeezed dry**

1 **small garlic clove, minced**

¼ **teaspoon salt**

2 **(7-inch) whole wheat pita breads, halved and warmed**

▲ 1½ **cups coarsely shredded skinless cooked chicken breast**

▲ 1 **large tomato, thinly sliced**

▲ ½ **small red onion, thinly sliced**

▲ 4 **small green leaf lettuce leaves**

1. To make sauce, stir together yogurt, cucumber, garlic, and salt in small bowl.

2. Spread half of yogurt sauce evenly inside pita halves. Layer chicken, tomato, onion, and lettuce evenly in pita halves. Top evenly with remaining yogurt sauce.

PER SERVING (½ SANDWICH): 201 grams, 207 Cal, 3 g Total Fat, 1 g Sat Fat, 0 g Trans Fat, 46 mg Chol, 385 mg Sod, 25 g Total Carb, 5 g Total Sugar, 3 g Fib, 22 g Prot, 78 mg Calc.

▲ **HEALTHY EXTRA** Serve these sandwiches with a refreshing fruit salad of sliced kiwifruit, raspberries, and orange sections topped with very thinly sliced fresh mint.

Turkey BLTs

4 PointsPlus value
Per Serving

LEVEL Basic

PREP 10 min

COOK 10 min

SERVES 4

2 tablespoons fat-free mayonnaise

Grated zest of ½ lemon

4 slices whole wheat bread, toasted

▲ 4 green leaf lettuce leaves

▲ 8 ounces thinly sliced no-salt added fat-free skinless turkey breast

▲ 1 large tomato, sliced

4 slices turkey bacon, crisp cooked

1. Stir together mayonnaise and lemon zest in cup.

2. Spread mayonnaise mixture evenly on 2 slices of bread. Layer bread evenly with lettuce, turkey, tomato, and bacon. Cover with remaining 2 slices bread. Cut sandwiches in half.

PER SERVING (½ SANDWICH): 158 grams, 166 Cal, 5 g Total Fat, 1 g Sat Fat, 0 g Trans Fat, 39 mg Chol, 329 mg Sod, 17 g Total Carb, 3 g Total Sugar, 3 g Fib, 16 g Prot, 29 mg Calc.

▲ **HEALTHY EXTRA** Make this classic sandwich even more flavorful by adding thin slices of sweet onion.

Niçoise-Style
Tuna Sandwiches

Niçoise-Style Tuna Sandwiches

LEVEL Basic

PREP 20 min

COOK None

SERVES 4

1 **(8-ounce) crusty round bread, split**

2 **tablespoons red wine vinegar**

2 **teaspoons extra-virgin olive oil**

¼ **teaspoon black pepper**

▲ 2 **(5-ounce) cans low-sodium water-packed chunk light tuna, drained**

▲ 1 **hard-cooked large egg, peeled and chopped**

▲ 2 **scallions, thinly sliced**

8 **pitted Kalamata olives, chopped**

1 **tablespoon capers, drained and finely chopped**

▲ 2 **tomatoes, thinly sliced**

½ **cup lightly packed fresh basil leaves**

1. Remove enough bready center from bread halves to leave 1-inch shell. (Reserve bready center for another use, such as for making fresh bread crumbs.)

2. To make dressing, whisk together vinegar, oil, and pepper in cup. Brush over cut sides of bread.

3. Flake tuna in medium bowl. Stir in egg, scallions, olives, and capers.

4. On bottom of bread, layer half of tomato slices and basil leaves. Spread tuna mixture on top of basil. Arrange remaining tomato slices and basil over tuna. Cover with top of bread. Wrap tightly in foil; refrigerate at least 2 hours. Cut into 4 wedges to serve.

PER SERVING (1 WEDGE): 203 grams, 260 Cal, 8 g Total Fat, 1 g Sat Fat, 0 g Trans Fat, 104 mg Chol, 628 mg Sod, 20 g Total Carb, 4 g Total Sugar, 2 g Fib, 27 g Prot, 49 mg Calc.

 FYI This tasty sandwich is **perfect picnic food**, as it can be prepared early in the day and kept in a cooler for up to 8 hours.

Fruits & Vegetables

▶ **Have fruit with every meal.** At breakfast, top whole-grain cereal with sliced banana or berries. Have an apple or nectarine with lunch. And after dinner, treat yourself to poached pears or spiced fruit compote.

▶ **Challenge your taste buds.** Every week, peruse the produce section at the grocery store and choose a new fruit or vegetable to try—star fruit, Asian pears, rutabaga, beet greens, jicama, or whatever strikes your fancy. It's a fun, easy way to discover new favorites and add them to your healthy-foods repertoire.

▶ **Stash fruits and vegetables in your freezer.** Whether you're tossing together a last-minute fruit salad, making a quick topping for cake or frozen yogurt (with berries, mango, pineapple, and peaches), or stir-frying veggies and meat, it's smart to have frozen produce on hand.

Turkey, Roasted Pepper, and Ricotta Panini

PointsPlus value
Per Serving

LEVEL Basic

PREP 25 min

COOK 5 min

SERVES 2

▲ ½ **cup fat-free ricotta cheese, drained**

4 **slices whole grain bread**

▲ 1 **cup lightly packed baby spinach**

▲ ⅓ **cup roasted red peppers (not packed in oil), thickly sliced**

4 **large fresh basil leaves**

▲ 4 **(1-ounce) slices no-salt added fat-free skinless turkey breast**

1. Spread ricotta evenly over 2 slices of bread. Layer half of spinach, roasted peppers, basil, and turkey over cheese. Cover with remaining 2 slices bread. Gently flatten each sandwich.

2. Lightly spray large heavy skillet with nonstick spray and set over medium heat. Add sandwiches and top with weight such as another pan. Cook until bread is crisp and golden, about 3 minutes. Turn sandwiches over; weight them and cook until second side is crisp and golden, about 3 minutes longer.

PER SERVING (1 SANDWICH): 222 grams, 267 Cal, 4 g Total Fat, 1 g Sat Fat, 0 g Trans Fat, 40 mg Chol, 505 mg Sod, 33 g Total Carb, 6 g Total Sugar, 4 g Fib, 24 g Prot, 161 mg Calc.

FYI For a classic "grilled" effect, cook the **panini** in an electric panini maker or in a stovetop grill pan.

Salmon-Veggie Sandwiches

PointsPlus value

Per Serving

LEVEL Basic

PREP 15 min

COOK None

SERVES 2

▲ 1   (7 ½-ounce) can no-salt added salmon, drained and flaked

3   tablespoons fat-free mayonnaise

▲ ½   cup chopped celery

▲ ½   cup finely chopped red onion

2   tablespoons chopped fresh dill

2   teaspoons Dijon mustard

Grated zest and juice of 1 lemon

4   slices whole wheat bread, toasted

▲ 4   tomato slices

▲ ½   cup lightly packed baby arugula or spinach

1. Stir together salmon, mayonnaise, celery, onion, dill, mustard, and lemon zest and juice in medium bowl.

2. Spread salmon mixture evenly over 2 slices of toast. Top each with 2 tomato slices and ¼ cup of arugula. Cover sandwiches with remaining slices toast.

PER SERVING (1 SANDWICH): 315 grams, 306 Cal, 10 g Total Fat, 2 g Sat Fat, 0 g Trans Fat, 23 mg Chol, 704 mg Sod, 39 g Total Carb, 8 g Total Sugar, 7 g Fib, 21 g Prot, 293 mg Calc.

▲ **HEALTHY EXTRA** Add very thin slices of English (seedless) cucumber to the sandwiches.

Oven-Roasted Vegetable Burritos

LEVEL Basic

PREP 25 min

ROAST 40 min

SERVES 4

▲ 1   **(1-pound) eggplant, cut into ¾-inch chunks**

▲ 2   **red bell peppers, cut into ¾-inch pieces**

▲ 1   **zucchini, cut into ¾-inch chunks**

½   **teaspoon salt**

4   **(8-inch) low-fat whole wheat tortillas, warmed**

▲ 1   **cup thinly sliced romaine lettuce**

▲ 1   **large tomato, seeded and chopped**

▲ 1   **jalapeño pepper, seeded and minced**

½   **cup shredded reduced-fat Monterey Jack cheese**

1. Preheat oven to 450°F.

2. Toss together eggplant, bell peppers, zucchini, and salt in large roasting pan; spray with nonstick spray. Toss again and spread in pan. Roast vegetables, stirring occasionally, until tender and lightly browned, about 40 minutes.

3. Spoon one-fourth of roasted vegetables on each tortilla. Top with one-fourth of lettuce, tomato, jalapeño, and Monterey Jack. Fold two opposite sides of each tortilla over to enclose filling.

PER SERVING (1 BURRITO): 349 grams, 215 Cal, 6 g Total Fat, 2 g Sat Fat, 0 g Trans Fat, 10 mg Chol, 557 mg Sod, 39 g Total Carb, 9 g Total Sugar, 7 g Fib, 9 g Prot, 227 mg Calc.

▲ **HEALTHY EXTRA** If you are feeling super-hungry, spread fat-free refried beans over each tortilla before adding the vegetables (¼ cup of fat-free refried beans with each serving will increase the *PointsPlus* value by *1*).

Vegetable-Cheese Quesadillas

7 PointsPlus value
Per Serving

LEVEL Basic

PREP 20 min

BROIL/COOK 25 min

SERVES 4

- ▲ 2 **small zucchini, thinly sliced**
- ▲ 2 **red bell peppers, sliced**
- ½ **teaspoon dried oregano**
- 8 **(8-inch) fat-free whole wheat tortillas**
- 8 **tablespoons shredded reduced-fat Montery Jack cheese**
- ▲ 3 **scallions, thinly sliced**
- ▲ ½ **cup fat-free salsa**

1. Preheat broiler. Line baking sheet with nonstick foil.

2. Spread zucchini and bell peppers on prepared baking sheet. Lightly spray with nonstick spray; sprinkle with oregano. Broil 5 inches from heat, stirring once or twice, until vegetables are softened and lightly charred, about 12 minutes.

3. Place 4 tortillas on work surface. Top each with 1 tablespoon of Monterey Jack, one-fourth of vegetable mixture, one-fourth of scallions, and 1 tablespoon of cheese. Cover with remaining 4 tortillas, lightly pressing down.

4. Spray large nonstick skillet with nonstick spray and set over medium heat. Add 1 quesadilla and cook until crisp and cheese begins to melt, about 1½ minutes per side. Transfer to cutting board; keep warm. Cook remaining 3 quesadillas. Cut each into 4 wedges. Serve with salsa.

PER SERVING (4 WEDGES AND 2 TABLESPOONS SALSA): 242 grams, 234 Cal, 4 g Total Fat, 2 g Sat Fat, 0 g Trans Fat, 10 mg Chol, 657 mg Sod, 51 g Total Carb, 7 g Total Sugar, 6 g Fib, 12 g Prot, 164 mg Calc.

Vegetable-Cheese
Quesadillas

Chicken and Mushroom Pizza

7 PointsPlus value
Per Serving

LEVEL Basic

PREP 25 min

BAKE/COOK 25 min

SERVES 6

3 **tablespoons grated Parmesan cheese**

1 **tablespoon fat-free mayonnaise**

▲ 2 **teaspoons fat-free milk**

½ **teaspoon dried thyme**

▲ ½ **pound skinless boneless chicken breasts, cut crosswise into ½-inch slices**

½ **cup cornflake crumbs**

▲ 2 **cups thinly sliced white or cremini mushrooms**

¼ **teaspoon black pepper**

▲ ¾ **cup fat-free ricotta cheese**

1 **(10-ounce) prebaked thin whole wheat pizza crust**

½ **cup shredded part-skim mozzarella cheese**

1. Preheat oven to 450°F. Spray small baking dish with nonstick spray.

2. Stir together Parmesan, mayonnaise, milk, and thyme in medium bowl. Add chicken and toss to coat evenly.

3. Put cornflake crumbs in large zip-close plastic bag. Add chicken and shake bag until coated. Place chicken in prepared baking dish in single layer. Bake until golden brown and cooked through, about 5 minutes per side.

4. Meanwhile, spray large nonstick skillet with olive oil nonstick spray and set over medium-high heat. Add mushrooms and sprinkle with pepper; cook, stirring, until mushrooms release their juice and it is evaporated.

5. Spread ricotta over pizza crust. Top with mushrooms, chicken, and mozzarella. Bake until cheese is melted, about 15 minutes. Cut into 6 wedges

PER SERVING (1 WEDGE): 150 grams, 263 Cal, 6 g Total Fat, 3 g Sat Fat, 0 g Trans Fat, 33 mg Chol, 454 mg Sod, 33 g Total Carb, 4 g Total Sugar, 5 g Fib, 20 g Prot, 211 mg Calc.

▲ **HEALTHY EXTRA** Cook 1 zucchini and 1 red bell pepper, thinly sliced, along with the mushrooms in step 4.

Potato-Cheese Pita Pizzas

8 PointsPlus© value

Per Serving

LEVEL Basic

PREP 25 min

BAKE 10 min

SERVES 4

▲ **2 cups thinly sliced cooked potatoes**

2 teaspoons chopped fresh rosemary

¼ teaspoon black pepper

½ cup shredded fontina cheese

▲ **½ cup shredded fat-free mozzarella cheese**

4 (7-inch) whole wheat pita breads

1. Preheat oven to 450°F. Spray baking sheet with nonstick spray.

2. Toss together potatoes, rosemary, and pepper in medium bowl. Sprinkle fontina and mozzarella evenly over pita breads.

3. Divide potato mixture evenly among pitas; lightly spray with nonstick spray. Place pizzas on prepared baking sheet. Bake until potatoes are heated through and cheese is melted, about 8 minutes.

PER SERVING (1 PIZZA): 170 grams, 313 Cal, 6 g Total Fat, 3 g Sat Fat, 0 g Trans Fat, 18 mg Chol, 623 mg Sod, 52 g Total Carb, 2 g Total Sugar, 7 g Fib, 16 g Prot, 217 mg Calc.

Ham, Brown Rice, and Pea Salad

7 PointsPlus value
Per Serving

LEVEL Basic
PREP 25 min
COOK 25 min
SERVES 6

▲ 1 **cup brown rice**

▲ 2 **cups frozen baby peas**

▲ 1 **(½-pound) piece low-sodium fat-free ham, cut into ½-inch pieces**

▲ 2 **cups cherry tomatoes, halved**

½ **cup shredded Gruyère cheese**

▲ 2 **scallions, thinly sliced**

2 **tablespoons chopped fresh mint**

3 **tablespoons champagne vinegar or cider vinegar**

2 **teaspoons olive oil**

¼ **teaspoon black pepper**

1. Cook rice according to package directions, omitting salt if desired and adding peas during last 5 minutes of cooking time. Drain rice with peas in colander; let cool.

2. Transfer rice mixture to serving bowl. Add remaining ingredients; toss to coat evenly.

PER SERVING (ABOUT 1½ CUPS): 260 grams, 277 Cal, 8 g Total Fat, 3 g Sat Fat, 0 g Trans Fat, 31 mg Chol, 519 mg Sod, 34 g Total Carb, 3 g Total Sugar, 5 g Fib, 16 g Prot, 125 mg Calc.

▲ **HEALTHY EXTRA** Spoon this salad over Boston, Bibb, or butter lettuce leaves and serve with whole radishes with their leaves attached.

Asparagus-Chicken Salad with Lemon Dressing

5 PointsPlus value

Per Serving

LEVEL Basic

PREP 15 min

COOK 5 min

SERVES 6

▲ 1 **(1-pound) bunch asparagus, trimmed and cut into 1-inch pieces**

Grated zest and juice of 1 lemon

2 **tablespoons olive oil**

1 **large garlic clove, minced**

½ **teaspoon salt**

¼ **teaspoon black pepper**

▲ ¾ **pound cooked skinless boneless chicken breast, diced**

▲ 1 **(15 ½-ounce) can pinto beans, rinsed and drained**

▲ 1 **red bell pepper, chopped**

▲ 1 **cup grape tomatoes**

▲ 3 **scallions, sliced**

¼ **cup coarsely chopped fresh basil**

1. Put asparagus in steamer basket; set in large saucepan over 1 inch of boiling water. Cook, covered, just until tender, about 4 minutes. Drain in colander; rinse under cold running water. Drain again.

2. To make dressing, whisk together lemon zest and juice, oil, garlic, salt, and black pepper in serving bowl. Add asparagus and remaining ingredients; toss until mixed well.

PER SERVING (GENEROUS 1 CUP): 301 grams, 242 Cal, 3 g Total Fat, 1 g Sat Fat, 0 g Trans Fat, 72 mg Chol, 488 mg Sod, 19 g Total Carb, 4 g Total Sugar, 6 g Fib, 32 g Prot, 66 mg Calc.

▲ **HEALTHY EXTRA** Steam 1 cup of halved snow peas along with the asparagus, and add to the salad in step 2.

Asian Chicken Salad

Asian Chicken Salad

5 PointsPlus® value

Per Serving

LEVEL Basic
PREP 20 min
COOK 10 min
SERVES 4

▲ 4 **(5-ounce) skinless boneless chicken breasts**

½ **teaspoon salt**

¼ **teaspoon black pepper**

½ **teaspoon canola oil**

2 **tablespoons seasoned rice vinegar**

1 **tablespoon reduced-sodium soy sauce**

1 **tablespoon Asian (dark) sesame oil**

2 **teaspoons grated peeled fresh ginger**

▲ 3 **cups coleslaw mix**

▲ 1 **cup matchstick-cut carrots**

▲ 1 **small red bell pepper, thinly sliced**

▲ 4 **scallions, thinly sliced**

1. Sprinkle chicken with salt and pepper. Heat oil in large nonstick skillet over medium-high heat. Add chicken and cook until browned and cooked through, about 4 minutes per side. Transfer to plate. When cool enough to handle, thinly slice chicken on diagonal.

2. To make dressing, whisk together vinegar, soy sauce, sesame oil, and ginger in serving bowl. Add remaining ingredients; toss to coat evenly. Serve salad topped with chicken breast.

PER SERVING (1¼ CUPS): 215 grams, 231 Cal, 7 g Total Fat, 2 g Sat Fat, 0 g Trans Fat, 78 mg Chol, 684 mg Sod, 10 g Total Carb, 6 g Total Sugar, 3 g Fib, 30 g Prot, 54 mg Calc.

▲ **HEALTHY EXTRA** Add a thinly sliced yellow or green bell pepper to the salad for more crunch.

Turkey and Green Bean Salad with Yogurt-Mint Dressing

5 PointsPlus value
Per Servi•

LEVEL Basic
PREP 20 min
COOK 5 min
SERVES 4

▲ **1 pound green beans, trimmed and cut into 1-inch pieces**

▲ **1 (1-pound) piece no-salt added skinless roasted turkey breast, cut into bite-size pieces**

▲ **⅓ cup plain fat-free yogurt**

¼ cup chopped fresh parsley

2 tablespoons chopped fresh mint

Grated zest and juice of 1 lemon

¼ teaspoon salt

¼ teaspoon black pepper

▲ **4 large butter or Boston lettuce leaves**

▲ **1 (7-ounce) jar roasted red peppers (not packed in oil), drained and diced**

1. Put green beans in steamer basket; set in large saucepan over 1-inch of boiling water. Cook, covered, until tender, about 4 minutes. Drain in colander; rinse under cold running water. Drain again.

2. To make dressing, whisk together yogurt, parsley, mint, lemon zest and juice, salt, and black pepper in small bowl.

3. Arrange lettuce leaves on platter. Place turkey, green beans, and roasted peppers on top of lettuce. Spoon dressing over all.

PER SERVING (¼ OF SALAD): 315 grams, 206 Cal, 5 g Total Fat, 1 g Sat Fat, 0 g Trans Fat, 60 mg Chol, 354 mg Sod, 14 g Total Carb, 5 g Total Sugar, 5 g Fib, 30 g Prot, 101 mg Calc.

FYI You can substitute other dark green vegetables for the green beans, including small **broccoli florets, sugar snap peas, snow peas, or sliced zucchini.**

Grilled Tuna Niçoise Salad

7 PointsPlus value
Per Serving

LEVEL Basic
PREP 25 min
COOK/GRILL 15 min
SERVES 6

- ▲ 1 **pound small red potatoes, scrubbed**
- ▲ ½ **pound haricots verts (slender green beans), trimmed**
- ▲ 4 **(5-ounce) tuna steaks, ¾ inch thick**
- ¼ **teaspoon salt**
- 2 **tablespoons red wine vinegar**
- ▲ 2 **tablespoons reduced-sodium chicken broth**
- 1 **tablespoon olive oil**
- 1 **garlic clove, minced**
- ¼ **teaspoon black pepper**
- ▲ 1 **head Boston lettuce, leaves separated**
- ▲ 2 **tomatoes, cut into wedges**
- 12 **niçoise olives**
- ▲ 2 **hard-cooked large eggs, peeled and sliced**
- 1 **tablespoon nonpareil (tiny) capers, drained**

1. Spray grill rack with nonstick spray. Preheat grill to medium-high or prepare medium-high fire using direct method.

2. Meanwhile, put potatoes in large saucepan and add enough water to cover; bring to boil. Reduce heat and cook until tender, about 12 minutes, adding green beans during last 5 minutes of cooking time. Drain vegetables in colander and rinse under cold running water. Drain again.

3. Sprinkle tuna with salt. Place on grill rack and grill until fish is well marked but still pink in center, about 2 minutes per side for medium-rare. Transfer tuna to cutting board; let stand 5 minutes. Cut into ¼-inch slices.

4. To make dressing, whisk together vinegar, broth, oil, garlic, and pepper in small bowl. Arrange lettuce leaves on platter. Place tuna in center of platter. Arrange piles of potatoes, green beans, tomatoes, olives, and eggs around tuna. Drizzle dressing over all and sprinkle with capers.

PER SERVING (⅙ OF SALAD): 307 grams, 273 Cal, 7 g Total Fat, 1 g Sat Fat, 0 g Trans Fat, 115 mg Chol, 370 mg Sod, 23 g Total Carb, 4 g Total Sugar, 3 g Fib, 28 g Prot, 61 mg Calc.

 FYI Niçoise salad is usually made with canned tuna. Using **grilled tuna** takes this ever-popular salad to a new level.

Southwestern-Style Shrimp Caesar Salad

3 PointsPlus value
Per Serving

LEVEL Basic
PREP 25 min
COOK None
SERVES 6

¼ **cup fat-free mayonnaise**

¼ **cup grated Parmesan cheese**

1 **tablespoon lime juice**

1 **small garlic clove, minced**

¼ **teaspoon black pepper**

▲ 1 **large head romaine lettuce, torn into pieces**

¼ **cup coarsely chopped fresh cilantro**

▲ 1 **(4 ½-ounce) can chopped mild green chiles, drained**

1 **cup fat-free croutons**

▲ 1 **pound cooked large peeled and deveined shrimp**

1. To make dressing, whisk together mayonnaise, Parmesan, lime juice, garlic, and pepper in small bowl.

2. Combine romaine, cilantro, chiles, and croutons in serving bowl. Pour dressing over and toss to coat evenly. Top with shrimp.

PER SERVING (ABOUT 2½ CUPS): 192 grams, 152 Cal, 2 g Total Fat, 1 g Sat Fat, 0 g Trans Fat, 151 mg Chol, 517 mg Sod, 11 g Total Carb, 1 g Total Sugar, 2 g Fib, 20 g Prot, 130 mg Calc.

FYI For a more **elegant presentation**, use hearts of romaine lettuce instead of the torn pieces.

**Southwestern-Style
Shrimp Caesar Salad**

Classic Macaroni Salad

8
PointsPlus
value
Per Serving

LEVEL Basic
PREP 25 min
COOK 15 min
SERVES 4

△ **8** **ounces whole wheat elbow macaroni**

△ **1** **cup small broccoli florets**

△ **1** **large tomato, chopped**

△ **2** **celery stalks, thinly sliced**

△ **1** **small red bell pepper, chopped**

△ **2** **scallions, thinly sliced**

¼ **cup reduced-fat mayonnaise**

△ ¼ **cup fat-free sour cream**

1 **tablespoon lemon juice**

½ **teaspoon dried basil**

½ **teaspoon salt**

½ **teaspoon black pepper**

1. Cook macaroni according to package directions, omitting salt if desired. Drain in colander; rinse under cold running water. Drain again. Transfer to serving bowl.

2. Add broccoli, tomato, celery, bell pepper, and scallions to macaroni.

3. To make dressing, whisk together remaining ingredients in small bowl. Drizzle over macaroni mixture and toss to coat evenly.

PER SERVING (GENEROUS 1 CUP): 207 grams, 286 Cal, 6 g Total Fat, 1 g Sat Fat, 0 g Trans Fat, 5 mg Chol, 470 mg Sod, 52 g Total Carb, 6 g Total Sugar, 7 g Fib, 10 g Prot, 76 mg Calc.

Bean Salad–Topped Pita Wedges

PointsPlus© value

Per Serving

LEVEL Basic

PREP 20 min

BROIL 5 min

SERVES 4

▲ 1 **(15 ½-ounce) can no-salt added small white beans, rinsed and drained**

▲ 1 **small red bell pepper, chopped**

▲ 2 **scallions, chopped**

Grated zest and juice of 1 lemon

Pinch red pepper flakes

4 **(7-inch) whole wheat pita breads, each cut into 4 wedges**

▲ 16 **cherry tomatoes, halved**

4 **ounces reduced-fat soft goat cheese, crumbled**

1. Mix together beans, bell pepper, scallions, lemon zest and juice, and pepper flakes in medium bowl.

2. Preheat broiler.

3. Place pita wedges on baking sheet in single layer. Lightly spray with nonstick spray. Broil 5 inches from heat until crisp, about 5 minutes.

4. Spoon bean salad evenly on pita wedges. Top each with 2 tomato halves and sprinkle evenly with goat cheese.

PER SERVING (4 SALAD-TOPPED PITA WEDGES):
237 grams, 289 Cal, 5 g Total Fat, 2 g Sat Fat,
0 g Trans Fat, 5 mg Chol, 481 mg Sod, 52 g Total Carb,
3 g Total Sugar, 10 g Fib, 13 g Prot, 67 mg Calc.

Pork with Rice Noodles and Vegetables

Pork with Rice Noodles and Vegetables

LEVEL Basic
PREP 15 min
COOK 15 min
SERVES 4

3 ½ ounces rice stick noodles (½ of 7-ounce package)

▲ ½ cup reduced-sodium chicken broth

2 tablespoons cornstarch

2 tablespoons reduced-sodium soy sauce

2 teaspoons brown sugar

2 teaspoons canola oil

▲ ½ pound lean pork tenderloin, trimmed, sliced, and cut into thin strips

2 large garlic cloves, minced

▲ 6 ounces white mushrooms, sliced

▲ 2 cups broccoli slaw mix

▲ 1 cup matchstick-cut carrots

1. Plunge noodles into large bowl of hot water; let stand until softened, about 10 minutes; drain.

2. Meanwhile, to make sauce, whisk together broth, cornstarch, soy sauce, and brown sugar in small bowl until smooth.

3. Heat nonstick wok or deep large skillet over high heat until drop of water sizzles in pan; add 1 teaspoon of oil and swirl to coat pan. Add pork and stir-fry until browned, about 5 minutes. Add garlic and stir-fry until fragrant, about 30 seconds; transfer to medium bowl.

4. Heat remaining 1 teaspoon oil in wok. Add mushrooms, broccoli slaw, and carrots. Stir-fry until carrots are crisp-tender, about 6 minutes. Re-stir cornstarch mixture; add to wok along with pork. Stir-fry until sauce bubbles and thickens, about 2 minutes. Stir in noodles and stir-fry until heated through, about 2 minutes longer.

PER SERVING (ABOUT 1½ CUPS): 201 grams, 237 Cal, 5 g Total Fat, 1 g Sat Fat, 0 g Trans Fat, 32 mg Chol, 466 mg Sod, 33 g Total Carb, 5 g Total Sugar, 2 g Fib, 15 g Prot, 29 mg Calc.

FYI Rice stick noodles, also known as rice vermicelli or rice sticks, are made from rice flour. They only need a brief soak in very hot water to soften enough to eat. Rice sticks come in several different widths, from very thin to wide.

Activity

▶ **Make workout dates.** Instead of meeting a friend for a meal or a drink, head to the gym together. Take an exercise class together. Or take a hike or bike ride. You'll catch up with each other's news while moving your bodies—a healthy way of multitasking.

▶ **Move to energize yourself.** When you're feeling tired or down and you're not truly hungry, instead of automatically reaching for a snack, take a brisk walk in the sun or dance to your favorite tunes. Both forms of movement are likely to boost your mood and your energy level—and neither requires you to consume calories.

▶ **Fit it in.** Contrary to what you may have heard, there's no ideal time of day to exercise. The best time is the one that suits your personality and your schedule. Whenever possible, put exercising on your calendar as if it were a business or doctor's appointment so that you'll be more likely to treat it as a must-do.

Stovetop-Grilled Salmon with Mexican Corn Salad

8 PointsPlus© value
Per Serving

LEVEL Basic

PREP 15 min

ROAST/COOK 30 min

SERVES 4

▲ **2** (10-ounce) packages frozen corn kernels, thawed and patted dry

▲ **1** orange or green bell pepper, chopped

▲ **½** small red onion, thinly sliced

½ cup chopped fresh cilantro

▲ **1** jalapeño pepper, seeded and minced

3 tablespoons lime juice

1 tablespoon honey

1 teaspoon canola oil

¾ teaspoon salt

4 (¼-pound) salmon fillets

1. Preheat oven to 425°F. Spray jelly-roll pan with nonstick spray.

2. Spread corn in prepared pan. Roast, stirring occasionally, until lightly browned, about 20 minutes; let cool completely.

3. Mix together corn, bell pepper, onion, cilantro, jalapeño, lime juice, honey, oil, and ¼ teaspoon of salt in serving bowl.

4. Heat nonstick ridged grill pan over medium-high heat. Spray salmon fillets with olive oil nonstick spray; sprinkle with remaining ½ teaspoon salt. Place salmon in grill pan and cook until just opaque in center, about 4 minutes per side. Serve with corn salad.

PER SERVING (1 SALMON FILLET AND 1 CUP SALAD):
284 grams, 291 Cal, 6 g Total Fat, 1 g Sat Fat, 0 g Trans Fat, 57 mg Chol, 515 mg Sod, 37 g Total Carb, 8 g Total Sugar, 4 g Fib, 26 g Prot, 27 mg Calc.

FYI When **fresh corn** is in season, use it instead of the frozen. Look for ears with moist silk, which ensures the corn has been freshly picked. For this recipe you will need about 6 medium ears of corn to yield 3 cups of kernels.

Easy Salmon Cakes with Tartar Sauce

6 PointsPlus value
Per Serving

LEVEL Basic
PREP 30 min
COOK 10 min
SERVES 4

⅓ **cup + 3 tablespoons fat-free mayonnaise**

1 **tablespoon capers, drained and chopped**

1 **teaspoon lemon juice**

▲ 1 **(14 ¾-ounce) can salmon, drained**

▲ 1 **scallion, chopped**

▲ 1 **celery stalk, finely chopped**

¼ **cup +3 tablespoons plain dried bread crumbs**

Few drops hot pepper sauce

2 **teaspoons canola oil**

1. To make sauce, stir together ⅓ cup of mayonnaise, the capers, and lemon juice in serving bowl. Cover and refrigerate until ready to serve.

2. To make salmon cakes, with fork, mash salmon with bones in large bowl. Stir in remaining 3 tablespoons mayonnaise, the scallion, celery, 3 tablespoons of bread crumbs, and the hot sauce. Shape into 4 (½-inch-thick) patties. Cover and refrigerate until firm, about 1 hour.

3. Put remaining ¼ cup bread crumbs on sheet of wax paper. Coat patties with crumbs.

4. Heat oil in large nonstick skillet over medium heat. Add patties and cook until crisp and heated through, about 5 minutes per side. Serve with tartar sauce.

PER SERVING (1 SALMON CAKE AND ABOUT 1 TABLESPOON TARTAR SAUCE): 153 grams, 218 Cal, 11 g Total Fat, 2 g Sat Fat, 0 g Trans Fat, 57 mg Chol, 785 mg Sod, 14 g Total Carb, 3 g Total Sugar, 2 g Fib, 18 g Prot, 163 mg Calc.

FYI There's no need to buy packaged **bread crumbs** as you can easily make your own. Here's how: Tear leftover bread into small pieces and spread in a jelly-roll pan. Let stand until completely hard and dry, which will take about 1 day. (Or dry the bread in a 250°F oven for about 30 minutes.) Process the bread pieces in a food processor, in batches if needed, until crumbs form. The crumbs can be stored in the freezer in an airtight container or zip-close plastic freezer bag for up to 2 months.

Easy Salmon Cakes with Tartar Sauce

Mixed Grain and Cheddar Fritters

8 PointsPlus® value

Per Serving

LEVEL Basic
PREP 15 min
COOK 1 hr 10 min
SERVES 4

▲ **2** cups reduced-sodium vegetable broth

▲ **½** cup brown rice

▲ **½** cup quinoa, rinsed and drained

2 teaspoons olive oil

▲ **1** onion, finely chopped

▲ **2** carrots, shredded

▲ **½** cup fat-free egg substitute

½ cup shredded reduced-fat Cheddar cheese

3 tablespoons all-purpose flour

½ teaspoon dried thyme

½ teaspoon salt

¼ teaspoon black pepper

1. Bring broth to boil in medium saucepan; stir in rice. Reduce heat and cook, covered, 20 minutes. Stir in quinoa and cook, covered, until rice and quinoa are tender, about 20 minutes longer. Drain off any remaining liquid. Spread rice mixture on large plate and let cool.

2. Heat 1 teaspoon of oil in medium nonstick skillet over medium heat. Add onion and cook, stirring, until softened, about 5 minutes.

3. Mix together onion and all remaining ingredients except remaining oil in large bowl; stir in rice mixture.

4. Heat remaining 1 teaspoon oil on nonstick griddle or in large nonstick skillet over medium-high heat. Drop batter, in batches if needed, by ¼ cupfuls onto griddle Cook until golden, about 3 minutes per side. Repeat with remaining batter, making total of 16 fritters.

PER SERVING (4 FRITTERS): 335 grams, 308 Cal, 8 g Total Fat, 3 g Sat Fat, 0 g Trans Fat, 10 mg Chol, 584 mg Sod, 48 g Total Carb, 7 g Total Sugar, 5 g Fib, 13 g Prot, 162 mg Calc.

▲ **HEALTHY EXTRA** Turn these good-for-you fritters into a satisfying meal by serving them with a lettuce, tomato, and red onion salad dressed with lime juice and a pinch of salt.

Curried Bean-Walnut Burgers

6 PointsPlus® value
Per Serving

LEVEL Basic
PREP 25 min
COOK 10 min
SERVES 4

2 **teaspoons olive oil**
▲ 1 **onion, finely chopped**
▲ 1 **cup finely chopped celery**
2 **teaspoons curry powder**
¼ **teaspoon salt**
¼ **teaspoon hot pepper sauce or to taste**
▲ 1 **(15 ½-ounce) can red kidney beans, rinsed, drained, and mashed**
2 **cups fresh whole wheat bread crumbs (about 4 slices bread)**
▲ 1 **large egg**
¼ **cup finely chopped walnuts**
▲ 4 **Boston or butter lettuce leaves**
▲ 4 **thick tomato slices**

1. Heat 1 teaspoon of oil in medium nonstick skillet over medium heat. Add onion and celery; cook, stirring, until softened, about 5 minutes. Stir in curry powder, salt, and pepper sauce.

2. Mix together onion mixture, beans, bread crumbs, egg, and walnuts in large bowl. Shape mixture into 4 (½-inch-thick) patties and place on wax paper–lined plate. Refrigerate until firm, at least 30 minutes or up to 4 hours.

3. Heat remaining 1 teaspoon oil in large nonstick skillet over medium heat. Add patties and cook until golden and heated through, about 4 minutes per side.

4. Place 1 burger on each of 4 plates and place 1 lettuce leaf and 1 tomato slice alongside.

PER SERVING (1 BURGER, 1 LETTUCE LEAF, AND 1 TOMATO SLICE): 212 grams, 248 Cal, 10 g Total Fat, 2 g Sat Fat, 0 g Trans Fat, 53 mg Chol, 443 mg Sod, 32 g Total Carb, 6 g Total Sugar, 8 g Fib, 11 g Prot, 105 mg Calc.

▲ **HEALTHY EXTRA** After turning the burgers over, top each with a slice of fat-free Cheddar cheese. One (¾-ounce) slice of fat-free Cheddar cheese per serving will increase the *PointsPlus* value by *1*.

Chicken-Egg Drop Soup

Chicken-Egg Drop Soup

LEVEL Basic

PREP 10 min

COOK 20 min

SERVES 6

▲ 1 **(32-ounce) carton reduced-sodium chicken broth**

3 **garlic cloves, halved**

⅓ **cup cornstarch**

½ **cup water**

1 **tablespoon reduced-sodium soy sauce**

▲ 2 **large eggs, lightly beaten**

▲ 2 **cups lightly packed tender watercress sprigs**

▲ 1 **cup diced skinless cooked chicken breast**

▲ 2 **scallions, thinly sliced**

1. Combine broth and garlic in large saucepan and bring to boil. Reduce heat and simmer, covered, until flavors are blended, about 12 minutes. Discard garlic.

2. Meanwhile, stir together cornstarch and water in small bowl until smooth. Whisk cornstarch mixture into broth mixture. Cook, stirring constantly, until soup bubbles and thickens, about 3 minutes. Stir in soy sauce.

3. Reduce heat to low. Slowly pour in beaten eggs, while slowly stirring constantly in one direction so strands form. Stir in watercress, chicken, and scallions; cook until watercress is wilted and soup is heated through, about 2 minutes longer.

PER SERVING (1 CUP): 238 grams, 107 Cal, 3 g Total Fat, 1 g Sat Fat, 0 g Trans Fat, 91 mg Chol, 545 mg Sod, 8 g Total Carb, 1 g Total Sugar, 0 g Fib, 12 g Prot, 32 mg Calc.

▲ **HEALTHY EXTRA** Stir 1 large tomato, seeded and diced into the soup along with the watercress in step 3.

Sausage and Cabbage Soup

3 PointsPlus value
Per Servin

LEVEL Basic

PREP 15 min

COOK 50 min

SERVES 6

▲ 2   teaspoons olive oil

▲ 1   **onion, chopped**

▲ 1   **carrot, diced**

▲ 2   **celery stalks, diced**

1   **(6-ounce) piece low-fat kielbasa, thinly sliced**

3   **garlic cloves, minced**

8   **cups water**

¾   **teaspoon salt**

½   **teaspoon dried thyme**

¼   **teaspoon black pepper**

▲ 1   **small head green cabbage, shredded (about 8 cups)**

▲ 1   **all-purpose potato, peeled and shredded**

1. Heat oil in large saucepan over medium heat. Add onion, carrot, and celery; cook, stirring, until onion is softened, about 5 minutes. Add kielbasa and garlic; cook, stirring, until garlic is fragrant, about 30 seconds. Add water, salt, thyme, and pepper; bring to boil. Reduce heat and simmer, partially covered, 15 minutes.

2. Stir cabbage and potato into soup; return to boil. Reduce heat and simmer, partially covered, until vegetables are tender, about 30 minutes longer.

PER SERVING (GENEROUS 1 CUP): 521 grams, 113 Cal, 3 g Total Fat, 1 g Sat Fat, 0 g Trans Fat, 10 mg Chol, 580 mg Sod, 18 g Total Carb, 7 g Total Sugar, 4 g Fib, 6 g Prot, 82 mg Calc.

▲ **HEALTHY EXTRA** Make this soup even heartier by stirring in a 15 ½-ounce can of rinsed and drained white beans 10 minutes before the cooking time is up. This will increase the per-serving *PointsPlus* value by *2*.

Chunky Fish Chowder

LEVEL Basic

PREP 15 min

COOK 20 min

SERVES 4

2 teaspoons olive oil

▲ 1 onion, chopped

▲ 2 celery stalks, diced

▲ 1 pound all-purpose potatoes, peeled and diced

▲ 2 cups no-salt added chicken broth

1 (6-ounce) bottle clam juice

¾ teaspoon dried thyme

½ teaspoon salt

▲ 1 pound halibut or other firm white fish, cut into 1-inch chunks

▲ 1 (14 ½-ounce) can diced tomatoes

2 tablespoons chopped fresh parsley

1. Heat oil in large saucepan over medium heat. Add onion and celery; cook, stirring, until softened, about 5 minutes. Add potatoes, broth, clam juice, thyme, and salt; bring to boil. Reduce heat and simmer, partially covered, until potatoes are almost tender, about 8 minutes.

2. Add halibut and tomatoes to pot. Simmer, partially covered, stirring occasionally, until fish is just opaque in center, about 5 minutes. Stir in parsley.

PER SERVING (1½ CUPS): 519 grams, 284 Cal, 6 g Total Fat, 1 g Sat Fat, 0 g Trans Fat, 36 mg Chol, 665 mg Sod, 30 g Total Carb, 7 g Total Sugar, 5 g Fib, 29 g Prot, 103 mg Calc.

FYI A **chowder** is a thick and chunky soup that often contains seafood. The word "chowder" comes from the French word *chaudière*, which was the caldron that fishermen used when making soup.

Tuscan-Style Bean Soup

LEVEL Basic
PREP 15 min
COOK 10 min
SERVES 4

2   teaspoons olive oil
▲ 1   onion, chopped
▲ 1   carrot, diced
▲ 1   celery stalk, diced
2   garlic cloves, minced
▲ 1   (15 ½-ounce) can cannellini (white kidney) beans, rinsed and drained
▲ 2   cups reduced-sodium chicken broth
▲ 2   plum tomatoes, seeded and diced
¼   cup thinly sliced fresh basil
¼   teaspoon black pepper
¼   cup grated Parmesan cheese

1. Heat oil in medium saucepan over medium heat. Add onion, carrot, and celery; cook, stirring, until onion is softened, about 5 minutes. Add garlic and cook, stirring, until fragrant, about 30 seconds. Stir in beans and broth. With potato masher, coarsely mash cannellini beans.

2. Stir tomatoes, basil, and pepper into soup; bring to boil. Reduce heat and simmer, stirring occasionally, until heated through, about 4 minutes. Serve sprinkled with Parmesan.

PER SERVING (1 CUP): 303 grams, 139 Cal, 4 g Total Fat, 1 g Sat Fat, 0 g Trans Fat, 4 mg Chol, 517 mg Sod, 18 g Total Carb, 5 g Total Sugar, 5 g Fib, 8 g Prot, 115 mg Calc.

▲ **HEALTHY EXTRA** Chop a 4-ounce piece of cooked lean ham and stir it into the soup along with the tomatoes in step 2. This will increase the per-serving *PointsPlus* value by *1*.

Tuscan-Style
Bean Soup

3

Dinner

Mustard and Herb-Rubbed Beef
with Winter Vegetables

Mustard and Herb–Rubbed Beef with Winter Vegetables

8 PointsPlus® value
Per Serving

LEVEL Basic
PREP 25 min
ROAST 1 hr 30 min
SERVES 8

2   tablespoons chopped fresh thyme

2   garlic cloves, minced

2   tablespoons Dijon mustard

4   teaspoons olive oil

½   teaspoon black pepper

▲ 1   (2-pound) boneless eye-round roast, trimmed

1   tablespoon water

▲ 2   pounds small Yukon Gold potatoes, scrubbed and halved

▲ 1   pound carrots, cut on diagonal into 2-inch lengths

▲ 1   pound parsnips, cut on diagonal into 2-inch lengths

▲ 1   onion, cut into wedges

1. Preheat oven to 450°F. Spray very large roasting pan with nonstick spray.

2. Stir together thyme, garlic, mustard, oil, and pepper in small bowl. Place beef roast in prepared roasting pan. Rub half of herb mixture on top and sides of beef.

3. Stir water into remaining herb mixture until blended. Combine potatoes, carrots, parsnips, and onion in large bowl. Add herb mixture and toss to coat evenly. Scatter vegetables around meat.

4. Put roast in oven and reduce temperature to 350°F. Roast, stirring vegetables occasionally, until vegetables are tender and instant-read thermometer inserted into center of roast registers 145°F for medium, about 1 hour 30 minutes. Transfer roast to cutting board; let stand 10 minutes. Thinly slice across grain into 24 slices

PER SERVING (3 SLICES BEEF AND ⅛ OF VEGETABLES): 326 grams, 323 Cal, 7 g Total Fat, 2 g Sat Fat, 1 g Trans Fat, 52 mg Chol, 183 mg Sod, 39 g Total Carb, 8 g Total Sugar, 6 g Fib, 26 g Prot, 52 mg Calc.

FYI Spreading the herb mixture over the beef several hours ahead will make the roast even more flavorful. Loosely cover the roast with foil or plastic wrap and refrigerate until you're ready to pop it into the oven. Remove the foil before roasting.

Roasted Garlic–Rubbed Sirloin Steak

4 PointsPlus® value
Per Serving

LEVEL Basic

PREP 15 min

ROAST/BROIL 25 min

SERVES 4

5	large garlic cloves, unpeeled
1	teaspoon dried basil
½	teaspoon dried oregano
½	teaspoon salt
½	teaspoon black pepper
▲ 1	(1-pound) boneless sirloin steak, trimmed

1. Preheat oven to 400°F.

2. Loosely wrap garlic in foil and place in small baking dish. Roast until softened, about 15 minutes. Unwrap carefully.

3. When cool enough to handle, squeeze soft garlic from each clove into small bowl. Add basil, oregano, salt, and pepper, stirring until blended. Rub over both sides of steak.

4. Spray broiler rack with nonstick spray. Preheat broiler.

5. Place steak on prepared broiler rack. Broil 5 inches from heat until instant-read thermometer inserted into center of steak registers 145°F for medium, about 5 minutes per side. Transfer steak to cutting board and let stand 5 minutes. Slice across grain into 12 slices.

PER SERVING (3 SLICES): 76 grams, 151 Cal, 6 g Total Fat, 2 g Sat Fat, 1 g Trans Fat, 63 mg Chol, 338 mg Sod, 2 g Total Carb, 0 g Total Sugar, 0 g Fib, 22 g Prot, 26 mg Calc.

▲ **HEALTHY EXTRA** Round out this meal by serving steamed spinach and baked potatoes alongside. A 7-ounce baked potato with each serving will increase the *PointsPlus* value by *4*.

Hearty Beef-Bulgur Loaf

5 PointsPlus® value

Per Serving

LEVEL Basic

PREP 20 min

BAKE 30 min

SERVES 4

½ **cup warm water**

▲ ⅓ **cup fine bulgur**

▲ ¼ **cup moist-packed sun-dried tomatoes (not packed in oil), chopped**

▲ 1 **pound ground lean beef (5% fat or less)**

▲ ⅓ **cup plain fat-free yogurt**

▲ 1 **small onion, finely chopped**

1 **garlic clove, minced**

▲ 1 **large egg white**

½ **teaspoon dried oregano**

½ **teaspoon salt**

¼ **teaspoon black pepper**

1. Preheat oven to 375°F. Spray 4 x 8-inch loaf pan with nonstick spray.

2. Stir together water, bulgur, and sun-dried tomatoes in large bowl; let soak 10 minutes.

3. Add remaining ingredients to bulgur mixture, stirring to mix well. Press mixture into prepared loaf pan. Bake until instant-read thermometer inserted into center of loaf registers 160°F for well done, about 30 minutes. Let stand 10 minutes. Cut into 8 slices.

PER SERVING (2 SLICES): 169 grams, 214 Cal, 6 g Total Fat, 2 g Sat Fat, 1 g Trans Fat, 63 mg Chol, 439 mg Sod, 14 g Total Carb, 3 g Total Sugar, 3 g Fib, 27 g Prot, 48 mg Calc.

FYI **Bulgur** is whole wheat that has been steamed, dried, and ground to a fine, medium, or coarse texture. When soaked in warm water, it develops a chewy texture and tempting nutty flavor. Bulgur is a staple in Middle Eastern salads, stews, and side dishes, such as tabbouleh.

North African Meatball Stew

5
PointsPlus®
value
Per Serving

LEVEL Basic

PREP 20 min

COOK 35 min

SERVES 4

▲ **1 pound ground lean beef (5% fat or less)**

2 tablespoons finely chopped fresh cilantro

2 teaspoons ground cumin

½ **teaspoon salt**

¼ **teaspoon black pepper**

2 teaspoons olive oil

▲ **1 onion, chopped**

2 garlic cloves, minced

▲ **1 cup diced tomatoes**

¾ **cup water**

▲ **3 tablespoons tomato paste**

2 tablespoons lemon juice

2 tablespoons chopped fresh mint

1. Mix together beef, cilantro, 1 teaspoon of cumin, ¼ teaspoon of salt, and ⅛ teaspoon of pepper in large bowl just until well combined. With damp hands, shape mixture into 24 (1-inch) meatballs.

2. Heat oil in large nonstick skillet over medium heat. Add onion and cook, stirring, until softened, about 5 minutes. Add garlic and cook, stirring, until fragrant, about 30 seconds. Stir in tomatoes, water, tomato paste, and remaining 1 teaspoon cumin, ¼ teaspoon salt, and ⅛ teaspoon pepper; bring to boil.

3. Add meatballs to skillet. Reduce heat and simmer, covered, until meatballs are cooked through and sauce is thickened, about 30 minutes. Stir in lemon juice and sprinkle with mint.

PER SERVING (6 MEATBALLS AND ABOUT ⅔ CUP SAUCE): 276 grams, 217 Cal, 8 g Total Fat, 3 g Sat Fat, 1 g Trans Fat, 62 mg Chol, 434 mg Sod, 11 g Total Carb, 6 g Total Sugar, 3 g Fib, 25 g Prot, 44 mg Calc.

▲ **HEALTHY EXTRA** Serve this stew with a bowl of couscous (⅔ cup of cooked whole wheat couscous with each serving will increase the *PointsPlus* value by **3**).

North African Meatball Stew

Grilled Asian-Flavored Pork Skewers

LEVEL Basic

PREP 25 min

GRILL 10 min

SERVES 4

½   **cup water**

3   **tablespoons reduced-sodium soy sauce**

2   **tablespoons honey**

2   **tablespoons lime juice**

3   **garlic cloves, minced**

▲ 1   **(1-pound) lean pork tenderloin, trimmed and cut into 16 slices**

▲ 16   **white mushrooms**

▲ 16   **cherry tomatoes**

▲ 2   **cups hot cooked brown basmati rice**

2   **teaspoons sesame seeds, toasted**

1. Combine water, soy sauce, honey, lime juice, and garlic in large zip-close plastic bag; add pork. Squeeze out air and seal bag; turn to coat pork. Refrigerate, turning bag occasionally, at least 30 minutes or up to 6 hours.

2. Spray grill rack with nonstick spray. Preheat grill to medium-high or prepare medium-high fire using direct method.

3. Alternately thread pork, mushrooms, and tomatoes onto 8 (12-inch) metal skewers. Place skewers on grill rack and grill until pork is cooked through and vegetables are tender, about 4 minutes per side.

4. Sprinkle rice with sesame seeds and serve with pork.

PER SERVING (2 SKEWERS AND ½ CUP RICE):
276 grams, 324 Cal, 6 g Total Fat, 2 g Sat Fat, 0 g Trans Fat, 75 mg Chol, 175 mg Sod, 40 g Total Carb, 5 g Total Sugar, 3 g Fib, 29 g Prot, 13 mg Calc.

FYI The **easiest way to cut raw pork** into uniform slices is to first freeze it until firm, which will take about 30 minutes.

Mexican-Style Pork Stew

LEVEL Basic

PREP 15 min

COOK 1 hr 15 min

SERVES 4

1 teaspoon canola oil

3 garlic cloves, minced

1 cup water

¼ cup cider vinegar

¼ cup ancho chile powder

1 teaspoon dried oregano

¼ teaspoon salt

▲ 1 pound boneless center-cut lean pork loin, trimmed and cut into 1½-inch chunks

▲ 2 cups hot cooked brown rice

▲ ½ cup fat-free salsa

1. Heat oil in small saucepan over medium heat. Add garlic and cook, stirring, until fragrant, about 30 seconds. Stir in water, vinegar, chile powder, oregano, and salt until mixed well. Bring to boil. Reduce heat and simmer 10 minutes.

2. Transfer chile mixture to Dutch oven or large saucepan; stir in pork and bring to boil. Reduce heat and gently simmer, covered, until meat is very tender, about 1 hour. Serve with rice and salsa.

PER SERVING (SCANT 1 CUP PORK WITH SAUCE, ½ CUP RICE, AND 2 TABLESPOONS SALSA):
294 grams, 329 Cal, 11 g Total Fat, 3 g Sat Fat, 0 g Trans Fat, 63 mg Chol, 474 mg Sod, 33 g Total Carb, 5 g Total Sugar, 5 g Fib, 27 g Prot, 84 mg Calc.

FYI This stew's great flavor comes from the adobo sauce in which it is cooked. In Mexico, adobo is made with chiles, vinegar, and herbs. Ancho chiles, used in our adobo sauce, are the most commonly used chiles in Mexican cooking. They are the "sweetest" of all the dried chiles, with a flavor reminiscent of coffee, licorice, and raisins. Ancho chiles are available dried and ground in supermarkets and specialty food stores.

**Broiled Lamb Kebabs
with Spinach-Lentil Salad**

Broiled Lamb Kebabs with Spinach-Lentil Salad

8 PointsPlus® value

Per Serving

LEVEL Basic
PREP 15 min
COOK/BROIL 30 min
SERVES 4

4   **cups water**
▲ 1   **cup red lentils, picked over, rinsed, and drained**
2   **tablespoons lemon juice**
2   **teaspoons olive oil**
½   **teaspoon salt**
¼   **teaspoon black pepper**
1   **pound boneless lean lamb loin, trimmed and cut into 1-inch chunks**
¾   **teaspoon dried oregano**
12   **cherry tomatoes**
▲ 2   **cups lightly packed coarsely chopped spinach**
▲ 1   **small orange bell pepper, chopped**
▲ ½   **small red onion, thinly sliced**

1. Combine water and lentils in large saucepan; bring to boil. Reduce heat and simmer, covered, until lentils are tender, about 15 minutes; drain.

2. Meanwhile, to make dressing, whisk together lemon juice, oil, ¼ teaspoon of salt, and ⅛ teaspoon of black pepper in large bowl.

3. Spray broiler rack with nonstick spray. Preheat broiler.

4. Toss together lamb, oregano, and remaining ¼ teaspoon salt and ⅛ teaspoon black pepper in large bowl to coat evenly. Thread lamb and tomatoes evenly onto 4 (12-inch) metal skewers. Broil 5 inches from heat, turning, until lamb is cooked through and tomatoes are softened, about 8 minutes.

5. Add lentils, spinach, bell pepper, and onion to dressing; toss until mixed well. Spoon lentil salad onto platter and top with kebabs.

PER SERVING (1 KEBAB AND ¾ CUP LENTIL SALAD):
400 grams, 324 Cal, 8 g Total Fat, 2 g Sat Fat, 1 g Trans Fat, 65 mg Chol, 382 mg Sod, 31 g Total Carb, 3 g Total Sugar, 8 g Fib, 32 g Prot, 67 mg Calc.

▲ **HEALTHY EXTRA** Cook 2 carrots, cut into small dice, along with the lentils in step 1.

Lamb, Bacon, and Bean Chili

5 PointsPlus value
Per Servi

LEVEL Basic
PREP 15 min
COOK 1 hr 30 min
SERVES 6

3	slices turkey bacon
2	teaspoons olive oil
1	pound boneless lean lamb loin, trimmed and cut into ½-inch pieces
▲ 1	onion, chopped
2	garlic cloves, minced
1	tablespoon chili powder
2	teaspoons ground cumin
▲ 1	(28-ounce) can crushed tomatoes
1	teaspoon dried oregano
▲ 1	(15 ½-ounce) can pinto beans, rinsed and drained

1. Cook bacon in Dutch oven until crisp. Transfer to paper towels to drain. Wipe pot clean.

2. Heat 1 teaspoon of oil in Dutch oven over medium-high heat. Add lamb, in batches, and cook until lightly browned on all sides, about 10 minutes, transferring lamb to plate as it is browned.

3. Add remaining 1 teaspoon oil to pot. Add onion and cook, stirring, until softened, about 5 minutes. Add the garlic, chili powder, and cumin; cook, stirring, until fragrant, about 30 seconds. Stir in tomatoes and oregano; bring to boil. Reduce heat and simmer, covered, until lamb is very tender, about 1 hour. Stir in beans and simmer until heated through, about 5 minutes longer.

PER SERVING (1 CUP): 267 grams, 227 Cal, 7 g Total Fat, 2 g Sat Fat, 1 g Trans Fat, 50 mg Chol, 422 mg Sod, 20 g Total Carb, 6 g Total Sugar, 6 g Fib, 20 g Prot, 85 mg Calc.

▲ **HEALTHY EXTRA** Serve this robust chili over quinoa (⅔ cup of cooked quinoa per serving will increase the *PointsPlus* value by **3**).

Shepherd's Pie

6 PointsPlus® value
Per Serving

LEVEL Basic
PREP 25 min
COOK/BAKE 1 hr 10 min
SERVES 6

▲ 1 ½ **pounds Yukon Gold potatoes, peeled and cut into chunks**

▲ ½ **cup plain fat-free yogurt**

2 **tablespoons finely chopped fresh parsley**

¾ **teaspoon salt**

½ **teaspoon black pepper**

2 **teaspoons olive oil**

▲ 1 **large onion, chopped**

▲ ½ **pound ground lean beef (5% fat or less)**

½ **pound ground lean lamb**

▲ 1 **(14 ½-ounce) can diced tomatoes**

▲ 1 **cup frozen baby peas**

½ **teaspoon dried thyme**

1. Preheat oven to 375°F.

2. Put potatoes in large saucepan and add enough water to cover. Bring to boil. Reduce heat and simmer, partially covered, until potatoes are tender, about 20 minutes; drain. With potato masher, mash potatoes until smooth; stir in yogurt, parsley, ½ teaspoon of salt, and ¼ teaspoon of pepper.

3. Heat oil in large nonstick skillet over medium heat. Add onion; cook, stirring, until softened, about 5 minutes. Add beef and lamb; cook, breaking meat apart with spoon, until browned, about 7 minutes. Drain off fat.

4. Add tomatoes, peas, thyme, and remaining ¼ teaspoon salt and ¼ teaspoon pepper to skillet; bring to boil. Reduce heat and simmer, stirring occasionally, 10 minutes.

5. Spread meat mixture in 10-inch deep-dish pie plate or 1½-quart baking dish. Spread mashed potatoes on top. Bake until potatoes begin to brown and filling is bubbly, about 20 minutes. Let stand 10 minutes before serving.

PER SERVING (GENEROUS 1 CUP): 304 grams, 255 Cal, 5 g Total Fat, 2 g Sat Fat, 0 g Trans Fat, 43 mg Chol, 452 mg Sod, 33 g Total Carb, 8 g Total Sugar, 5 g Fib, 20 g Prot, 65 mg Calc.

 FYI **Shepherd's pie** was originally created as a way to use up leftovers from the traditional English Sunday roast.

French-Style Roast Chicken

LEVEL Basic

PREP 15 min

ROAST 1 hr 10 min

SERVES 6

2 **teaspoons herbes de Provence**

Grated zest of 1 lemon

2 **garlic cloves, minced**

1 **teaspoon olive oil**

1 **teaspoon salt**

½ **teaspoon black pepper**

1 **(3 ½-pound) roasting chicken, giblets removed**

▲ 1 **lemon, halved**

½ **bunch fresh rosemary or thyme**

▲ 1½ **pounds large red potatoes, scrubbed and cut into sixths**

▲ 1 **large tomato, coarsely chopped**

1. Preheat oven to 400°F. Place rack in roasting pan and spray with nonstick spray.

2. Stir together herbes de Provence, lemon zest, garlic, oil, ½ teaspoon of salt, and ¼ teaspoon of pepper in cup. Gently loosen skin from breast and thighs of chicken; spread herb paste on meat under skin. Put lemon and rosemary inside cavity. Tuck wings under and tie legs together with kitchen string. Place chicken, breast side up, on prepared rack.

3. Roast chicken until instant-read thermometer inserted into thigh (not touching bone) registers 165°F, about 1 hour 10 minutes. About 45 minutes before roasting time is up, scatter potatoes and tomato around chicken; sprinkle with remaining ½ teaspoon salt and ¼ teaspoon pepper; roast until tender.

4. Remove chicken from oven and let stand 10 minutes. Remove lemon and rosemary from cavity; discard. Carve chicken and serve with potatoes and tomato. Remove chicken skin before eating.

PER SERVING (⅙ OF CHICKEN AND ⅔ CUP VEGETABLES): 249 grams, 309 Cal, 9 g Total Fat, 2 g Sat Fat, 0 g Trans Fat, 90 mg Chol, 487 mg Sod, 24 g Total Carb, 3 g Total Sugar, 3 g Fib, 32 g Prot, 31 mg Calc.

▲ **HEALTHY EXTRA** Serve with a bowl of steamed greens, such as broccoli rabe, watercress, or broccoli.

French-Style
Roast Chicken

Orange and Honey-Marinated Chicken

Orange and Honey–Marinated Chicken

LEVEL Basic
PREP 20 min
BROIL 25 min
SERVES 6

Grated zest of 1 orange

½ cup orange juice

¼ cup lime juice

2 tablespoons honey

½ teaspoon salt

¼ teaspoon black pepper

3 (6-ounce) bone-in chicken thighs, skinned

▲ 3 (6-ounce) bone-in chicken breasts, skinned

▲ 3 cups hot cooked whole wheat couscous

▲ 1 (11-ounce) can mandarin orange segments in juice, drained

¼ cup dried currants

1. Combine orange zest and juice, lime juice, honey, salt, and pepper in large zip-close plastic bag; add chicken. Squeeze out air and seal bag; turn to coat chicken. Refrigerate, turning bag occasionally, at least 1 hour or up to 6 hours.

2. Spray broiler rack with nonstick spray. Preheat broiler.

3. Remove chicken from marinade; discard marinade.

4. Place chicken on prepared broiler rack. Broil 7 inches from heat, turning, until chicken is browned and cooked though, about 25 minutes.

5. Mix together couscous, orange segments, and currants in serving bowl. Serve with chicken.

PER SERVING (1 PIECE CHICKEN AND ABOUT ¾ CUP COUSCOUS): 171 grams, 323 Cal, 6 g Total Fat, 2 g Sat Fat, 0 g Trans Fat, 70 mg Chol, 260 mg Sod, 40 g Total Carb, 9 g Total Sugar, 5 g Fib, 28 g Prot, 35 mg Calc.

FYI This flavorful chicken tastes even better when grilled over a medium fire that has been flavored with some cherry or apple wood chips. Soak about 1 cup of chips in cold water to cover for at least 30 minutes. Drain the chips before sprinkling them over the fire.

Crispiest Oven-Fried Chicken

5 PointsPlus® value
Per Servi[ng]

LEVEL Basic
PREP 15 min
BAKE 35 min
SERVES 6

⅓ **cup fat-free mayonnaise**

1 **tablespoon Dijon mustard**

2 **garlic cloves, minced**

½ **teaspoon salt**

¼ **teaspoon hot pepper sauce or to taste**

▲ 3 **(¾-pound) bone-in chicken breasts, skinned and cut crosswise in half**

¾ **cup cornflake crumbs**

1. Preheat oven to 375°F. Spray jelly-roll pan with nonstick spray.

2. Stir together mayonnaise, mustard, garlic, salt, and pepper sauce in large bowl. Add chicken and toss to coat evenly.

3. Put cornflake crumbs in large zip-close plastic bag. Add chicken, one piece at a time, and shake to coat; place chicken in prepared baking pan.

4. Lightly spray chicken with nonstick spray. Bake until golden brown and cooked through, about 35 minutes.

PER SERVING (1 PIECE CHICKEN): 109 grams, 186 Cal, 4 g Total Fat, 1 g Sat Fat, 0 g Trans Fat, 69 mg Chol, 507 mg Sod, 11 g Total Carb, 2 g Total Sugar, 0 g Fib, 26 g Prot, 18 mg Calc.

FYI If you happen to have cornflakes in your pantry, you can easily turn them into crumbs. Put them in a large zip-close plastic bag. Seal the bag squeezing out the air, and roll over the crumbs with a rolling pin until crushed. You'll need approximately 2 cups cornflakes to yield ¾ cup crumbs.

Rosemary Chicken with Cherry Tomato Sauce

5 PointsPlus value

Per Serving

LEVEL Basic

PREP 15 min

COOK 15 min

SERVES 4

▲ **4** (5-ounce) skinless boneless chicken breasts

1 tablespoon chopped fresh rosemary, thyme, or oregano

½ teaspoon salt

¼ teaspoon black pepper

2 teaspoons olive oil

1 large shallot, minced

2 garlic cloves, minced

▲ **1** pint cherry tomatoes, halved

▲ ¼ cup reduced-sodium vegetable broth

¼ cup chopped fresh basil

1. Place chicken between two pieces of plastic wrap. With meat pounder or rolling pin, pound to even thickness.

2. Sprinkle chicken with rosemary, salt, and pepper. Heat oil in large nonstick skillet over medium heat. Add chicken and cook until browned and cooked through, about 4 minutes per side. Transfer chicken to platter. Keep warm.

3. Add shallot and garlic to skillet. Cook, stirring, until softened, about 3 minutes. Add tomatoes and broth; cook, stirring occasionally, until tomatoes begin to soften, about 4 minutes longer. Stir in basil. Spoon sauce over chicken.

PER SERVING (1 CHICKEN BREAST AND ABOUT ½ CUP SAUCE): 194 grams, 197 Cal, 6 g Total Fat, 1 g Sat Fat, 0 g Trans Fat, 78 mg Chol, 396 mg Sod, 5 g Total Carb, 0 g Total Sugar, 1 g Fib, 30 g Prot, 30 mg Calc.

▲ **HEALTHY EXTRA** A bowl of whole wheat pasta, such as spaghetti or penne, is the perfect side for our Italian-inspired chicken dish. Be sure to spoon a little of the tomato sauce over the pasta (¾ cup of cooked whole wheat pasta per serving will increase the *PointsPlus* value by *3*).

Grilled Chicken and Asparagus with Capers and Basil

LEVEL Basic

PREP 20 min

COOK 10 min

SERVES 4

▲ 4 **(5-ounce) skinless boneless chicken breasts**

1 **teaspoon ground coriander**

½ **teaspoon salt**

¼ **teaspoon black pepper**

▲ 1 **(1-pound) bunch asparagus, trimmed**

1 **teaspoon olive oil**

▲ 1 **red onion, cut into wedges**

1 **tablespoon capers, rinsed**

2 **tablespoons sliced fresh basil**

Zest of ½ lemon

1. Spray grill rack with nonstick spray. Preheat grill to medium-high or prepare medium-high fire.

2. Sprinkle chicken with coriander, ¼ teaspoon of salt and the pepper. Place chicken on grill rack and grill, turning frequently until browned and cooked through, 8-10 minutes.

3. Toss together asparagus, oil, and remaining ¼ teaspoon salt until coated evenly. Spray onion with nonstick spray. Place asparagus and onion on grill rack and grill, turning often, until tender and well marked, about 4 minutes.

4. Toss together capers, basil, and lemon zest. Top chicken evenly with caper mixture and serve with asparagus and onion.

PER SERVING (1 CHICKEN BREAST AND ¼ OF ASPARAGUS AND ONION): 183 grams, 190 Cal, 5 g Total Fat, 1 g Sat Fat, 0 g Trans Fat, 78 mg Chol, 430 mg Sod, 5 g Total Carb, 0 g Total Sugar, 2 g Fib, 31 g Prot, 0 g Alcohol, 0 g Sugar Alcohol, 38 mg Calc.

▲ **HEALTHY EXTRA** Serve with a bowl of quinoa (⅔ cup of cooked quinoa per serving will increase the *PointsPlus* value by *3*).

Grilled Chicken and Asparagus with Capers and Basil

Easy Herbed Chicken Tenders

4 PointsPlus value Per Servi

LEVEL Basic
PREP 15 min
COOK 5 min
SERVES 4

1   **tablespoon olive oil**
1   **teaspoon dried thyme**
1   **teaspoon dried oregano**
1   **teaspoon dried basil**
1   **teaspoon dried sage**
½   **teaspoon salt**
¼   **teaspoon black pepper**
▲ 1   **pound chicken tenders**

1. Stir together all ingredients except chicken in cup. Put chicken in large bowl; spread herb mixture all over chicken.

2. Spray nonstick ridged grill pan with nonstick spray and set over medium-high heat. Add chicken and cook until golden brown and cooked through, about 3 minutes per side.

PER SERVING (¼ OF CHICKEN): 79 grams, 155 Cal, 6 g Total Fat, 1 g Sat Fat, 0 g Trans Fat, 63 mg Chol, 346 mg Sod, 1 g Total Carb, 0 g Total Sugar, 1 g Fib, 23 g Prot, 35 mg Calc.

▲ **HEALTHY EXTRA** Serve a salad of sliced fennel, orange slices, and thinly sliced red onion, drizzled with balsamic vinegar alongside the chicken.

Chicken Thighs with Spinach and Mushrooms

8
PointsPlus®
value

Per Serving

LEVEL Basic

PREP 15 min

COOK 25 min

SERVES 6

1 **(8-ounce) package no-yolk wide egg noodles**

1 **pound skinless boneless chicken thighs, trimmed and cut into 2-inch chunks**

½ **teaspoon salt**

¼ **teaspoon black pepper**

1 **teaspoon olive oil**

▲ 1 **(8-ounce) package white mushrooms, sliced**

▲ 1 **onion, chopped**

▲ ¾ **pound plum tomatoes, seeded and chopped**

▲ 1 ½ **cups reduced-sodium chicken broth**

▲ 1 **bunch baby spinach**

¼ **cup low-fat (1%) milk**

3 **tablespoons grated Parmesan cheese**

1. Cook egg noodles according to package directions, omitting salt if desired; drain. Keep warm.

2. Meanwhile, sprinkle chicken with ¼ teaspoon of salt and ⅛ teaspoon of pepper. Heat oil in large nonstick skillet over medium-high heat. Add chicken and cook, turning, until browned. Transfer to plate.

3. Add mushrooms and onion to skillet; cook, stirring, until mushrooms release their liquid, about 5 minutes. Return chicken to skillet. Stir in tomatoes, broth, and remaining ¼ teaspoon salt and ⅛ teaspoon pepper; bring to boil. Reduce heat and simmer, stirring, until chicken is cooked through, about 10 minutes.

4. Stir spinach, milk, and Parmesan into chicken mixture. Cook, stirring, until spinach is wilted. Serve over noodles.

PER SERVING (ABOUT 1½ CUPS): 344 grams, 328 Cal, 8 g Total Fat, 2 g Sat Fat, 0 g Trans Fat, 53 mg Chol, 558 mg Sod, 41 g Total Carb, 7 g Total Sugar, 5 g Fib, 25 g Prot, 110 mg Calc.

Feta-Stuffed Chicken Breasts

Feta-Stuffed Chicken Breasts

LEVEL Intermediate

PREP 25 min

BAKE 25 min

SERVES 4

▲ **2** ounces fat-free feta cheese, crumbled

▲ **2** moist-packed sun-dried tomatoes (not packed in oil), finely chopped

4 large fresh basil leaves, chopped

¼ teaspoon salt

¼ teaspoon black pepper

¼ cup panko (Japanese bread crumbs)

▲ **4** (5-ounce) skinless boneless chicken breasts

4 teaspoons fat-free mayonnaise

1. Preheat oven to 425°F. Spray nonstick baking pan with nonstick spray.

2. With fork, mix together feta, sun-dried tomatoes, basil, salt, and pepper in small bowl until blended. Spread panko on sheet of wax paper.

3. With small sharp knife, cut pocket, about 2 ½ inches long, in each chicken breast. Put one-fourth of cheese mixture into each pocket; press edges closed. Brush top of each breast with mayonnaise. Press coated side of chicken, one breast at a time, in crumbs. Place, coated side up, in prepared baking pan.

4. Lightly spray crumbs with nonstick spray. Bake until chicken is cooked through and crust is golden, about 25 minutes.

PER SERVING (1 STUFFED CHICKEN BREAST):
117 grams, 187 Cal, 4 g Total Fat, 1 g Sat Fat, 0 g Trans Fat, 79 mg Chol, 508 mg Sod, 5 g Total Carb, 1 g Total Sugar, 0 g Fib, 32 g Prot, 67 mg Calc.

▲ **HEALTHY EXTRA** Spray a skillet with nonstick spray and cook sliced white mushrooms and baby spinach until the mushrooms are softened and the spinach is wilted. Serve alongside the chicken.

Chinese-Style Barbecued Chicken

6 PointsPlus™ value
Per Serving

LEVEL Basic
PREP 15 min
BAKE 40 min
SERVES 6

▲ 1   **small onion, finely chopped**

⅓   **cup ketchup**

2   **tablespoons brown sugar**

2   **tablespoons hoisin sauce**

2   **tablespoons reduced-sodium soy sauce**

2   **tablespoons dry sherry or dry vermouth**

2   **garlic cloves, minced**

6   **(½-pound) whole chicken legs, skinned**

1. Preheat oven to 400°F. Line shallow baking pan with nonstick foil.

2. Stir together all ingredients except chicken in large bowl. Add chicken and toss to coat evenly.

3. Place chicken in prepared baking pan; brush any remaining sauce over chicken. Cover pan with foil; bake 20 minutes. Remove foil and bake until chicken is glazed and cooked through, about 20 minutes longer.

PER SERVING (1 CHICKEN LEG): 133 grams, 243 Cal, 9 g Total Fat, 2 g Sat Fat, 0 g Trans Fat, 96 mg Chol, 539 mg Sod, 11 g Total Carb, 6 g Total Sugar, 0 g Fib, 28 g Prot, 22 mg Calc.

▲ **HEALTHY EXTRA** Serve this finger lickin'–good chicken with a refreshing cucumber salad. Peel, halve, and seed 2 large cucumbers. Slice and sprinkle with unseasoned rice vinegar and a pinch of red pepper flakes.

Healthy Oils

Eat fat at every meal. It doesn't take much—a few chopped walnuts on your breakfast cereal, olive oil in your salad dressing at lunch, fatty fish (like tuna) for dinner—but it's wise to incorporate some fat into every meal to add flavor, aid in your body's absorption of fat-soluble vitamins, and feel satisfied.

Think about spreads. Instead of relying on mayo or cream cheese for sandwich spreads, try smearing mashed avocado or a heart-healthy nut butter (such as almond, cashew, hazelnut, or peanut) on your bread.

Put flaxseeds in your fridge. Whether you grind them yourself or buy them ground, keep flaxseeds around (refrigerated for optimum freshness) and sprinkle on cereal or salads or use it in homemade breads or pancake batter or as a crusty coating for salmon or chicken. Flaxseeds are rich in fiber and a good source of healthy omega-3 fatty acids.

Turkey Sausages with Warm Potato Salad

6 PointsPlus value

Per Serving

LEVEL Basic
PREP 15 min
COOK 35 min
SERVES 6

▲ 1½ **pounds red potatoes, scrubbed and cut into 1-inch chunks**

3 **tablespoons dry vermouth or reduced-sodium chicken broth**

3 **tablespoons white wine vinegar**

1 **tablespoon extra-virgin olive oil**

1 **tablespoon coarse-grained Dijon mustard**

¼ **teaspoon black pepper**

▲ 1 **cup grape tomatoes, halved**

▲ 2 **scallions, finely chopped**

⅓ **cup chopped fresh parsley**

2 **tablespoons chopped fresh dill**

1 **tablespoon nonpareil (tiny) capers, drained and chopped**

6 **sweet or hot Italian-style turkey sausages**

1. Put potatoes in large saucepan and add enough water to cover. Bring to boil. Reduce heat and cook, covered, until potatoes are tender, about 15 minutes; drain well. Transfer hot potatoes to serving bowl and sprinkle with vermouth; toss to coat evenly. Set aside, tossing potatoes occasionally.

2. To make dressing, whisk together vinegar, oil, mustard, and pepper until blended. Drizzle over potatoes, tossing to mix well. Add tomatoes, scallions, parsley, dill, and capers; gently toss to mix well.

3. Heat nonstick ridged grill pan over medium-high heat. Add sausages and cook, turning, until nicely marked and cooked through, about 15 minutes. Serve with potato salad.

PER SERVING (1 SAUSAGE AND ABOUT ¾ CUP POTATO SALAD): 227 grams, 251 Cal, 10 g Total Fat, 3 g Sat Fat, 0 g Trans Fat, 0 mg Chol, 528 mg Sod, 26 g Total Carb, 3 g Total Sugar, 3 g Fib, 14 g Prot, 23 mg Calc.

▲ **HEALTHY EXTRA** Serve the sausages and potato salad with a bowl of steamed whole green beans.

Turkey Sausages with
Warm Potato Salad

Lemony Arctic Char with Black Bean Salad

6 PointsPlus value

Per Serving

LEVEL Basic
PREP 30 min
BROIL 5 min
SERVES 4

Grated zest of 1 lemon

¼ **cup lemon juice**

1 **tablespoon olive oil**

2 **teaspoons honey**

½ **teaspoon salt**

½ **teaspoon black pepper**

▲ 4 **(¼-pound) arctic char fillets, skinned**

▲ 1 **(15 ½-ounce) can black beans, rinsed and drained**

▲ 2 **cups fresh or thawed frozen corn kernels**

▲ 1 **orange bell pepper, diced**

▲ ½ **cup chopped red onion**

¼ **cup chopped fresh cilantro**

1. To make dressing, whisk together lemon zest and juice, oil, honey, salt, and black pepper in small bowl.

2. Transfer 3 tablespoons of dressing to large zip-close plastic bag; add arctic char. Squeeze out air and seal bag; turn to coat fish. Refrigerate, turning bag occasionally, about 30 minutes. Reserve remaining dressing.

3. To make black bean salad, toss together remaining ingredients and dressing in serving bowl.

4. Spray broiler rack with nonstick spray. Preheat broiler.

5. Remove arctic char from marinade; discard marinade. Place fish on prepared broiler rack. Broil 5 inches from heat until fish is just opaque in center, about 3 minutes per side. Serve with black bean salad

PER SERVING (1 ARCTIC CHAR FILLET AND ABOUT ¾ CUP SALAD): 292 grams, 247 Cal, 5 g Total Fat, 1 g Sat Fat, 0 g Trans Fat, 71 mg Chol, 474 mg Sod, 31 g Total Carb, 4 g Total Sugar, 7 g Fib, 21 g Prot, 42 mg Calc.

FYI **Arctic char is similar to salmon.** It is mostly farm-raised using ecologically-friendly methods, which puts it high on the sustainable seafood list.

Pepper-Crusted Arctic Char with Mango

LEVEL Basic
PREP 5 min
COOK 10 min
SERVES 4

▲ 4   **(5-ounce) arctic char fillets, skinned**

½   **teaspoon salt**

3   **tablespoons coarse black pepper**

▲ 1   **mango, peeled, pitted, and cut into 8 wedges**

1. Sprinkle arctic char with salt. Spread pepper on sheet of wax paper. Lightly press both sides of arctic char fillets into pepper to coat.

2. Spray nonstick ridged grill pan with nonstick spray and set over medium-high heat. Place arctic char and mango in grill pan and cook until fish is just opaque in center and mango is marked, about 4 minutes per side for the fish and 1 minute per side for mango.

PER SERVING (1 ARCTIC CHAR FILLET AND 2 MANGO WEDGES): 171 grams, 164 Cal, 4 g Total Fat, 1 g Sat Fat, 0 g Trans Fat, 94 mg Chol, 360 mg Sod, 12 g Total Carb, 8 g Total Sugar, 2 g Fib, 20 g Prot, 0 g Alcohol, 0 g Sugar Alcohol, 36 mg Calc.

▲ **HEALTHY EXTRA** Round out this meal with baked potatoes and steamed broccoli florets. A 7-ounce baked potato with each serving will increase the *PointsPlus* value by *4*.

Cod with Puttanesca Sauce

Cod with Puttanesca Sauce

LEVEL Basic

PREP 15 min

COOK 30 min

SERVES 4

▲ 6 **ounces whole wheat spaghetti**

2 **teaspoons olive oil**

3 **garlic cloves, minced**

▲ 1 **(28-ounce) can whole tomatoes in puree with basil**

2 **tablespoons pitted Kalamata olives, chopped**

2 **tablespoons chopped fresh parsley**

1 **tablespoon nonpareil (tiny) capers, drained**

1 **teaspoon dried oregano**

½ **teaspoon red pepper flakes or to taste**

▲ 1 **(1-pound) cod fillet or halibut steak, cut into 4 equal pieces**

1. Cook spaghetti according to package directions, omitting salt if desired. Drain and keep warm.

2. Meanwhile, heat oil in deep large skillet over medium heat. Add garlic and cook, stirring, until fragrant, about 30 seconds. Add tomatoes, olives, parsley, capers, oregano, and pepper flakes; bring to boil. Reduce heat and simmer, breaking up tomatoes with side of wooden spoon, until sauce is slightly thickened, about 10 minutes.

3. Add cod to skillet, spooning sauce over fish; simmer, covered, until cod is just opaque in center, about 8 minutes.

4. Transfer spaghetti to serving bowl. Spoon some sauce over pasta. Serve with fish and remaining sauce.

PER SERVING (1 COD FILLET, ¾ CUP SPAGHETTI, AND ¾ CUP SAUCE): 406 grams, 305 Cal, 5 g Total Fat, 1 g Sat Fat, 0 g Trans Fat, 43 mg Chol, 552 mg Sod, 39 g Total Carb, 6 g Total Sugar, 7 g Fib, 26 g Prot, 77 mg Calc.

FYI **Capers** are the unopened flower buds of a spiny bush that grows all over the Mediterranean. The smallest capers are called nonpareil. Their bold flavor makes a little bit go a long way. Capers are available in supermarkets packed in small bottles alongside the olives and pickles.

Oven-Crisped Cod

LEVEL Basic

PREP 10 min

ROAST 10 min

SERVES 4

▲ 1 **(1-pound) cod fillet or halibut steak, cut into 4 equal pieces**

¼ **cup chopped fresh parsley**

Juice of 1 lemon

2 **tablespoons all-purpose flour**

2 **teaspoons olive oil**

½ **teaspoon dried oregano**

½ **teaspoon salt**

¼ **teaspoon black pepper**

Pinch cayenne

1. Preheat oven to 450°F. Spray 7 x 11-inch baking dish with nonstick spray.

2. Place fish in prepared baking dish.

3. Mix together remaining ingredients in small bowl. Spoon flour mixture evenly over fish. Bake until fish is just opaque in center and crisp on top, about 10 minutes.

PER SERVING (1 COD FILLET): 101 grams, 122 Cal, 3 g Total Fat, 1 g Sat Fat, 0 g Trans Fat, 43 mg Chol, 354 mg Sod, 4 g Total Carb, 1 g Total Sugar, 0 g Fib, 19 g Prot, 21 mg Calc.

▲ **HEALTHY EXTRA** Serve this crispy lemon-infused fish with a sliced tomato and red onion salad.

Tuna with Fennel, Orange, and Olive Salad

6
PointsPlus©
value
Per Serving

LEVEL Basic
PREP 25 min
COOK 5 min
SERVES 4

▲ 1 large fennel bulb, very thinly sliced

▲ 1 navel orange, sectioned

▲ 2 scallions, chopped

12 pitted Kalamata olives, coarsely chopped

¼ cup red wine vinegar

4 teaspoons olive oil

½ teaspoon salt

¼ teaspoon black pepper

▲ 4 (5-ounce) tuna steaks, ¾ inch thick

1. To make salad, toss together fennel, orange sections, scallions, olives, vinegar, 2 teaspoons oil, ¼ teaspoon of salt, and ⅛ teaspoon of pepper in serving bowl.

2. Sprinkle tuna with remaining ¼ teaspoon salt and ⅛ teaspoon pepper. Heat remaining 2 teaspoons oil in nonstick skillet over medium heat. Add tuna and cook until browned on outside but still pink in center, about 3 minutes per side. Serve with fennel salad.

PER SERVING (1 TUNA STEAK AND ABOUT 1 CUP SALAD): 208 grams, 255 Cal, 9 g Total Fat, 1 g Sat Fat, 0 g Trans Fat, 66 mg Chol, 542 mg Sod, 7 g Total Carb, 4 g Total Sugar, 2 g Fib, 35 g Prot, 59 mg Calc.

FYI To section an orange, cut a slice off the top and bottom end. Stand the orange and slice off the peel and white pith, turning the orange as you cut. Hold the fruit over a bowl to catch the juices and cut between the membranes to release the sections, allowing the sections and juice to fall into the bowl.

Mushroom and Spinach–Stuffed Trout

LEVEL Intermediate
PREP 30 min
COOK/BAKE 25 min
SERVES 4

2   teaspoons olive oil
▲ ¼   **pound white mushrooms, chopped**
▲ 1   **onion, chopped**
▲ 1   **(10-ounce) package frozen chopped spinach, thawed and squeezed dry**
½   **cup shredded reduced-fat Cheddar cheese**
▲ 4   **(5-ounce) skinless rainbow trout fillets**
¼   **teaspoon salt**
¼   **teaspoon black pepper**
½   **cup fresh whole wheat bread crumbs (about 1 slice bread)**

1. Preheat oven to 450°F. Spray 9-inch square baking dish with nonstick spray.

2. Heat oil in medium skillet over medium heat. Add mushrooms and onion; cook, stirring, until mushrooms release their liquid and it is evaporated, about 10 minutes. Stir in spinach and Cheddar.

3. Lay trout, skinned side up, on work surface; sprinkle with salt and pepper. Top fillets evenly with spinach mixture. Roll up fish and place, seam side down, in prepared baking dish. Sprinkle bread crumbs evenly over fish; spray with nonstick spray.

4. Bake until trout is just opaque in center and crumbs are golden, about 15 minutes.

PER SERVING (1 STUFFED TROUT FILLET):
272 grams, 286 Cal, 12 g Total Fat, 4 g Sat Fat, 0 g Trans Fat, 85 mg Chol, 418 mg Sod, 11 g Total Carb, 3 g Total Sugar, 4 g Fib, 33 g Prot, 288 mg Calc.

FYI This elegant dish is **ideal company food**. The fish can be prepared up to 8 hours ahead, then covered and refrigerated until ready to bake. Baked tomato halves or steamed asparagus make the perfect accompaniments.

Cajun-Seasoned Catfish

LEVEL Basic
PREP 15 min
BAKE 10 min
SERVES 4

- ▲ ¼ **cup yellow cornmeal**
- 3 **tablespoons all-purpose flour**
- 2 **teaspoons Cajun seasoning**
- ½ **teaspoon salt**
- ½ **teaspoon black pepper**
- ▲ 1 **large egg**
- ▲ 4 **(¼-pound) catfish fillets**

1. Preheat oven to 450°F. Spray broiler pan or heavy baking sheet with nonstick spray.

2. Mix together cornmeal, flour, Cajun seasoning, salt, and pepper on sheet of wax paper.

3. Lightly beat egg in large shallow bowl or pie plate. Dip fish, one piece at a time, into egg, then coat in cornmeal mixture, pressing lightly so it adheres.

4. Place fish in prepared pan. Lightly spray with nonstick spray. Bake until just opaque in center and crisp and golden on outside, about 10 minutes.

PER SERVING (1 CATFISH FILLET): 115 grams, 162 Cal, 4 g Total Fat, 1 g Sat Fat, 0 g Trans Fat, 114 mg Chol, 470 mg Sod, 12 g Total Carb, 0 g Total Sugar, 1 g Fib, 19 g Prot, 18 mg Calc.

▲ **HEALTHY EXTRA** Corn on the cob and a steamed dark green leafy vegetable, such as collard greens, mustard greens, or Swiss chard suit this fish to a tee. One medium ear of corn, grilled or steamed, with each serving will increase the *PointsPlus* value by *2*.

Shrimp and Chicken Jambalaya

7
PointsPlus
value

Per Servi

LEVEL Basic
PREP 25 min
COOK 55 min
SERVES 6

 2 teaspoons olive oil
▲ 1 large onion, chopped
▲ 1 red bell pepper, chopped
▲ 1 celery stalk, chopped
 2 garlic cloves, minced
▲ 1 cup brown rice
▲ 1 14 ½-ounce can reduced-sodium chicken broth
▲ 1 (14 ½-ounce) can diced tomatoes
 ½ teaspoon dried thyme
 ½ teaspoon salt
 ⅛ teaspoon cayenne
▲ ½ pound skinless boneless chicken breasts, cut into ¾-inch chunks
▲ ½ pound medium shrimp, peeled and deveined
▲ 4 cups small broccoli florets
▲ 1 (2-ounce) piece cooked low-sodium fat-free ham, diced
▲ 3 scallions, thinly sliced

1. Heat oil in nonstick Dutch oven over medium heat. Add onion, bell pepper, and celery; cook, stirring, until softened, about 5 minutes. Stir in garlic and cook, stirring, until fragrant, about 30 seconds. Add rice and cook, stirring, 1 minute.

2. Add broth, tomatoes, thyme, salt, and cayenne to pot; bring to boil. Reduce heat and simmer, covered, until rice is almost tender, about 30 minutes.

3. Add chicken to pot. Cook, covered, 10 minutes. Stir in shrimp, broccoli, and ham. Cook, covered, until shrimp are just opaque, chicken is cooked through, and rice is tender, about 5 minutes longer. Serve sprinkled with scallions.

PER SERVING (⅙ OF JAMBALAYA): 415 grams, 265 Cal, 5 g Total Fat, 1 g Sat Fat, 0 g Trans Fat, 82 mg Chol, 662 mg Sod, 35 g Total Carb, 6 g Total Sugar, 6 g Fib, 22 g Prot, 79 mg Calc.

 FYI **To save some prep time,** buy two (8-ounce) packages of broccoli florets from the produce section of your supermarket.

Asparagus and Shrimp Stir-Fry

LEVEL Basic

PREP 15 min

COOK 15 min

SERVES 6

▲ 1   **cup reduced-sodium chicken broth**

   2   **tablespoons reduced-sodium soy sauce**

   1   **tablespoon cornstarch**

   2   **teaspoons canola oil**

▲ 1   **(1-pound) bunch asparagus, trimmed and cut into 1½-inch lengths**

▲ 2   **red bell peppers, thinly sliced**

▲ 1   **pound large shrimp, peeled and deveined, tails left on if desired**

▲ 1   **bunch scallions, trimmed and cut into 2-inch lengths**

   2   **tablespoons minced peeled fresh ginger**

   3   **garlic cloves, minced**

   2   **teaspoons Asian (dark) sesame oil**

▲ 4   **cups hot cooked brown rice**

1. Stir together broth, soy sauce, and cornstarch in small bowl until smooth.

2. Heat nonstick wok or deep large nonstick skillet over medium-high heat until drop of water sizzles in pan; add oil and swirl to coat pan. Add asparagus and bell peppers; stir-fry until crisp-tender, about 5 minutes. Add shrimp and scallions; stir-fry until shrimp are just opaque in center about 4 minutes. Add ginger and garlic: stir-fry until fragrant, about 1 minute.

3. Re-stir cornstarch mixture; add to wok along with sesame oil. Stir-fry until sauce bubbles and thickens, about 1 minute. Serve with rice.

PER SERVING (1⅓ CUPS SHRIMP WITH VEGETABLES AND ⅔ CUP RICE): 334 grams, 268 Cal, 5 g Total Fat, 1 g Sat Fat, 0 g Trans Fat, 112 mg Chol, 448 mg Sod, 38 g Total Carb, 3 g Total Sugar, 4 g Fib, 18 g Prot, 62 mg Calc.

FYI When it comes to stir-fries, preparing the ingredients takes more time than the actual cooking. Put all of the prepped ingredients in bowls alongside the stove for easy access.

Scallops with Tomatoes and Feta Cheese

LEVEL Basic
PREP 15 min
COOK/BROIL 25 min
SERVES 4

2 teaspoons olive oil
▲ 1 onion, chopped
3 garlic cloves, minced
▲ 2 large plum tomatoes, chopped
⅓ cup dry white or red wine
½ teaspoon dried oregano
½ teaspoon salt
¼ teaspoon black pepper
▲ 1 pound sea scallops
1 tablespoon ouzo, pernod, or anisette
2 ounces reduced-fat feta cheese, crumbled
▲ 2 cups hot cooked brown rice

1. Heat oil in large nonstick skillet over medium heat. Add onion and cook, stirring, until softened, about 5 minutes. Add garlic and cook, stirring, until fragrant, about 30 seconds. Add tomatoes, wine, oregano, salt, and pepper; bring to boil. Reduce heat and simmer, until flavors are blended, about 10 minutes.

2. Add scallops to tomato mixture; cook until just opaque in center, about 5 minutes. Stir in ouzo.

3. Preheat broiler.

4. Turn scallop mixture into heatproof casserole dish. Sprinkle with feta. Broil 5 inches from heat until cheese is lightly browned and softened, about 2 minutes. Serve over rice.

PER SERVING (ABOUT 1 CUP SCALLOP MIXTURE AND ½ CUP RICE): 284 grams, 308 Cal, 8 g Total Fat, 2 g Sat Fat, 0 g Trans Fat, 39 mg Chol, 682 mg Sod, 33 g Total Carb, 5 g Total Sugar, 3 g Fib, 24 g Prot, 79 mg Calc.

FYI Ouzo (OO-zoh), pernod (pehr-NOH), and anisette (an-ih-SEHT) are clear, sweet, anise-flavored liqueurs that are often served as aperitifs. Ouzo is made in Greece, pernod is produced in France, and anisette is made in Italy.

Fisherman's Wharf Seafood Stew

Fisherman's Wharf Seafood Stew

4 PointsPlus® value
Per Serving

LEVEL Basic

PREP 20 min

COOK 25 min

SERVES 6

2   teaspoons olive oil

▲ 1   red bell pepper, chopped

▲ 6   scallions, thinly sliced

▲ 2   celery stalks, chopped

3   garlic cloves, thinly sliced

▲ 1   (14 ½-ounce) can diced tomatoes

1   cup water

1   cup dry white wine or dry vermouth

Pinch red pepper flakes

▲ 1   cup frozen corn kernels, thawed

▲ ¾   pound large shrimp, peeled and deveined, tails left on if desired

▲ ½   pound mussels, scrubbed and debearded

▲ ½   pound halibut fillet, cut into 1 ½-inch chunks

1. Heat oil in nonstick Dutch oven over medium heat. Add bell pepper, scallions, celery, and garlic; cook, stirring, until softened, about 5 minutes. Add tomatoes, water, wine, and pepper flakes; bring to boil. Reduce heat and simmer, covered, until flavors are blended, about 10 minutes. Stir in corn.

2. Add shrimp, mussels, and halibut to pot; return to boil. Reduce heat and simmer, covered, until mussels open and shrimp are just opaque, about 5 minutes. Discard any mussels that do not open. Divide stew evenly among 6 large shallow soup bowls.

PER SERVING (1⅓ CUPS): 314 grams, 189 Cal, 4 g Total Fat, 1 g Sat Fat, 0 g Trans Fat, 106 mg Chol, 334 mg Sod, 14 g Total Carb, 4 g Total Sugar, 3 g Fib, 23 g Prot, 75 mg Calc.

Mussels in Saffron Tomato Broth

LEVEL Basic

PREP 15 min

COOK 15 min

SERVES 5

¼ **teaspoon saffron threads**

¼ **cup hot water**

1 **tablespoon olive oil**

⅓ **cup minced shallots**

3 **garlic cloves, minced**

▲ 1 **(14 ½-ounce) can no-salt added diced tomatoes**

½ **cup dry white wine**

¼ **teaspoon black pepper**

▲ 4 **pounds mussels, scrubbed and debearded**

2 **tablespoons chopped fresh parsley**

1. Stir together saffron and water in cup.

2. Heat oil in Dutch oven over medium heat. Add shallots and cook, stirring, until softened, about 4 minutes. Add garlic and cook, stirring, until fragrant, about 30 seconds.

3. Add tomatoes, wine, saffron water, and pepper to pot; bring to boil. Add mussels and simmer, covered, until they open, about 5 minutes, transferring mussels to large bowl as they open. Discard any mussels that do not open. Divide mussels evenly among 4 large, shallow bowls. Pour mussel broth over and sprinkle evenly with parsley.

PER SERVING (ABOUT 20 MUSSELS AND ABOUT ⅓ CUP BROTH): 440 grams, 333 Cal, 10 g Total Fat, 2 g Sat Fat, 0 g Trans Fat, 90 mg Chol, 951 mg Sod, 18 g Total Carb, 9 g Total Sugar, 2 g Fib, 39 g Prot, 107 mg Calc.

FYI The hairy filaments that protrude from **mussels** are known as the "beard." To remove it, pinch the beard between your fingers and firmly pull or cut it off with scissors. Debeard mussels just before cooking.

Living the Good Health Guidelines

Whole Grains

▶ **Fill up on fiber.** Aim to get 25 to 35 grams of fiber a day from whole grains, beans, peas, lentils, vegetables, and fruit by including at least one food from these categories in every meal and snack. Fiber increases your feeling of fullness and slows the time it takes food to pass through your digestive system.

▶ **Opt for whole wheat.** Whenever you have a choice of breads, tortillas, bagels, or pizza crusts, choose whole wheat or rye over the white-flour version. You'll get more in the way of flavor, the feeling of fullness, and nutrients from every bite.

▶ **Pack up your whole grains.** Place a reasonable portion of whole-grain crackers, air-popped popcorn, or whole-grain breakfast cereal (such as shredded wheat) and a few nuts in a sandwich bag and take it with you to replenish your energy and keep hunger at bay when you're on the run.

Two Grain-Stuffed Peppers

6 PointsPlus value Per Serving

LEVEL Basic
PREP 25 min
COOK/BAKE/BROIL 1 hr
SERVES 4

2   teaspoons olive oil
▲ 1 onion, chopped
1   cup water
▲ ⅓ cup amaranth, rinsed
⅓   cup white rice
▲ 1 cup canned small white beans, rinsed and drained
⅓   cup chopped fresh flat-leaf parsley
▲ 1 jalapeño pepper, seeded and minced
¼   teaspoon salt
¼   teaspoon black pepper
▲ 2 large bell peppers, cut in half through stem end and seeded
2   ounces reduced-fat feta cheese, cut into ¼-inch dice

1. Preheat oven to 350°F. Spray 8 x 12-inch baking dish with nonstick spray.

2. Heat oil in large nonstick saucepan over medium heat. Add onion and cook, stirring, until softened, about 5 minutes. Add water, amaranth, and rice; bring to boil. Reduce heat and simmer, covered, until amaranth and rice are tender and liquid is absorbed, about 20 minutes. Stir in beans, parsley, jalapeño, salt, and black pepper.

3. Divide amaranth mixture evenly among bell pepper halves; place in prepared baking dish. Cover dish tightly with foil; bake until bell peppers are tender and filling is heated through, about 30 minutes.

4. Preheat broiler.

5. Uncover baking dish. Sprinkle feta evenly over filling; broil 5 inches from heat until cheese is lightly browned and softened, about 3 minutes.

PER SERVING (1 STUFFED PEPPER HALF): 331 grams, 256 Cal, 5 g Total Fat, 2 g Sat Fat, 0 g Trans Fat, 5 mg Chol, 421 mg Sod, 43 g Total Carb, 5 g Total Sugar, 8 g Fib, 10 g Prot, 98 mg Calc.

FYI **Amaranth**, once thought of only as a common weed, is now appreciated as a nutritious high-protein grain. Amaranth greens can be used in soups and salads.

Vegetarian Moussaka

LEVEL Intermediate

PREP 20 min

BAKE/COOK 50 min

SERVES 4

▲ 1 **(1-pound) eggplant, unpeeled and cut into ¼-inch rounds**

2 **teaspoons olive oil**

▲ 1 **onion, chopped**

3 **garlic cloves, minced**

▲ 1 **(28-ounce) can whole tomatoes**

½ **cup TVP (textured vegetable protein)**

▲ 1 **red bell pepper, chopped**

¼ **cup dry white wine**

¼ **teaspoon salt**

¼ **teaspoon black pepper**

3 **tablespoons all-purpose flour**

▲ 1½ **cups fat-free milk**

▲ 1 **large egg**

⅛ **teaspoon ground nutmeg**

½ **cup grated Parmesan cheese**

1. Preheat oven to 375°F. Spray 8 x 12-inch baking dish with nonstick spray. Spray large baking sheet with nonstick spray.

2. Arrange eggplant slices on prepared baking sheet in single layer. Bake until softened, about 20 minutes.

3. Meanwhile, to make tomato sauce, heat oil in large nonstick saucepan over medium heat. Add onion and garlic; cook, stirring, until onion is golden, about 8 minutes. Add tomatoes with their juice, TVP, bell pepper, wine, salt, and black pepper; bring to boil. Reduce heat and simmer, breaking up tomatoes with side of wooden spoon, until liquid is almost evaporated, about 20 minutes.

4. To make white sauce, whisk together flour and ¼ cup of milk in small saucepan until smooth; whisk in remaining 1¼ cups milk. Cook over medium heat, stirring constantly, until mixture bubbles and thickens, about 3 minutes. Remove saucepan from heat. Beat egg and nutmeg in small bowl; stir about ½ cup of hot milk mixture into beaten egg, then stir into saucepan until mixed well.

5. Layer eggplant in prepared baking dish; spoon tomato sauce on top. Pour white sauce over and spread evenly; sprinkle with Parmesan. Bake until moussaka is heated through and top is golden, about 20 minutes. Let stand 5 minutes before serving.

PER SERVING (¼ OF MOUSSAKA): 523 grams, 291 Cal, 8 g Total Fat, 3 g Sat Fat, 0 g Trans Fat, 63 mg Chol, 764 mg Sod, 34 g Total Carb, 18 g Total Sugar, 9 g Fib, 23 g Prot, 367 mg Calc.

FYI TVP (textured vegetable protein) is dried, granular soybean meal that substitutes nicely for meat in vegetarian dishes. It is sold in bulk and in 1-pound packages in supermarkets and natural food stores.

Broccoli-Polenta Casserole

LEVEL Basic

PREP 20 min

COOK/BAKE 40 min

SERVES 6

1   **tablespoon olive oil**

▲ 2   **onions, chopped**

3   **garlic cloves, minced**

▲ 1   **bunch broccoli, stems chopped and tops cut into small florets**

▲ ¾   **cup reduced-sodium vegetable broth**

⅛   **teaspoon cayenne**

3½ **cups water**

½   **teaspoon salt**

▲ 1   **cup yellow cornmeal**

⅓   **cup grated Romano cheese**

1. Preheat oven to 375°F. Spray 10-inch pie plate or casserole dish with nonstick spray.

2. Heat oil in deep large nonstick skillet over medium heat. Add onions and cook, stirring, until golden, about 7 minutes. Add garlic and cook, stirring, until fragrant, about 30 seconds. Add broccoli, broth and cayenne; cook, stirring occasionally, until broccoli is tender and most of liquid is evaporated, about 10 minutes longer. Remove skillet from heat

3. Meanwhile, to make polenta, bring water and salt to boil in large nonstick saucepan. Reduce heat to medium; slowly whisk in cornmeal in thin, steady stream. Reduce heat to low and cook, stirring constantly with wooden spoon, until very thick, about 10 minutes. Pour polenta into prepared pie plate and spread evenly.

4. Spoon broccoli mixture over polenta; sprinkle with Romano. Bake until heated through and browned, about 20 minutes. Let stand 5 minutes before serving.

PER SERVING (⅙ OF CASSEROLE): 355 grams, 169 Cal, 4 g Total Fat, 1 g Sat Fat, 0 g Trans Fat, 2 mg Chol, 319 mg Sod, 29 g Total Carb, 6 g Total Sugar, 6 g Fib, 7 g Prot, 87 mg Calc.

FYI The **casserole** can be assembled up to several hours before baking and set aside at room temperature.

Winter Vegetable Casserole

8 PointsPlus value
Per Serving

LEVEL Basic

PREP 20 min

COOK 45 min

SERVES 6

1   tablespoon olive oil

▲ 1   large onion, chopped

▲ 3   carrots, cut into small dice

▲ 3   celery stalks, cut into small dice

▲ 2   parsnips, cut into small dice

3   garlic cloves, minced

▲ 2   (15 ½-ounce) cans red kidney beans, rinsed and drained

▲ 1   cup reduced-sodium vegetable broth

1   teaspoon dried oregano

¾   teaspoon salt

½   teaspoon black pepper

▲ 4   cups hot cooked quinoa

1. Heat oil in nonstick Dutch oven over medium heat. Add onion, carrots, celery, and parsnips; cook, stirring, until onion is golden, about 7 minutes. Add garlic and cook, stirring, until fragrant, about 30 seconds.

2. Stir in all remaining ingredients except quinoa; bring to boil. Reduce heat and simmer, covered, until vegetables are tender and flavors are blended, about 30 minutes. Serve over quinoa.

PER SERVING (1½ CUPS CASSEROLE AND ⅔ CUP QUINOA): 326 grams, 337 Cal, 5 g Total Fat, 5 g Sat Fat, 0 g Trans Fat, 0 mg Chol, 572 mg Sod, 62 g Total Carb, 10 g Total Sugar, 12 g Fib, 14 g Prot, 118 mg Calc.

▲ **HEALTHY EXTRA** Begin the meal with a generous mixed greens, cucumber, and radicchio salad dressed with lemon juice.

Lentil-Bean Chili

8 PointsPlus® value
Per Serving

LEVEL Basic

PREP 15 min

COOK 45 min

SERVES 6

1	tablespoon canola oil
▲ 1	large onion chopped
▲ 1	(28-ounce) can crushed tomatoes
▲ 1	cup reduced-sodium vegetable broth
▲ 1½	cups lentils, picked over, rinsed, and drained
▲ 1	cup fresh or frozen corn kernels
▲ 1	red bell pepper, diced
▲ 1	green bell pepper, diced
2	teaspoons chili powder or to taste
2	teaspoons ground cumin
½	teaspoon salt
▲ 1	(15 ½-ounce) can black beans, rinsed and drained
▲ 6	tablespoons fat-free sour cream

1. Heat oil in nonstick Dutch oven over medium heat. Add onion and cook, stirring, until softened, about 5 minutes. Add tomatoes, broth, and lentils; bring to boil. Reduce heat and simmer, covered, 20 minutes.

2. Add corn, bell peppers, chili powder, cumin, and salt to pot. Return to boil. Reduce heat and simmer, covered, until lentils and vegetables are tender, about 15 minutes. Add beans and cook until heated through, about 2 minutes longer. Serve with sour cream.

PER SERVING (ABOUT 1¼ CUPS CHILI AND 1 TABLESPOON SOUR CREAM): 487 grams, 344 Cal, 4 g Total Fat, 0 g Sat Fat, 0 g Trans Fat, 5 mg Chol, 630 mg Sod, 58 g Total Carb, 13 g Total Sugar, 18 g Fib, 21 g Prot, 165 mg Calc.

▲ **HEALTHY EXTRA** Make this chili even more delicious by topping it with chopped scallions and fresh cilantro.

Stir-Fried Tempeh and Vegetables with Barley

LEVEL Basic

PREP 20 min

COOK 10 min

SERVES 6

1   (8-ounce) package tempeh, cut into ¼-inch slices

▲ 1   cup reduced-sodium vegetable broth

¼   cup creamy peanut butter

3   tablespoons reduced-sodium soy sauce

1   tablespoon grated peeled fresh ginger

2   teaspoons canola oil

▲ ½   pound shiitake mushrooms, stemmed and quartered

▲ ½   pound snow peas

▲ 1   yellow bell pepper, thinly sliced

▲ 6   scallions, cut into 2-inch lengths

▲ 3   cups hot cooked pearl barley

1. Half-fill medium saucepan with water and bring to boil; add tempeh. Reduce heat and simmer until softened, about 5 minutes; drain.

2. Meanwhile, to make sauce, whisk together broth, peanut butter, soy sauce, and ginger in small bowl until blended.

3. Heat nonstick wok or deep large skillet over high heat until drop of water sizzles in pan; add oil and swirl to coat pan. Add mushrooms, snow peas, and bell pepper; stir-fry until bell pepper is crisp-tender, about 3 minutes. Add scallions and sauce; stir-fry until vegetables are coated with peanut sauce and scallions are softened, about 2 minutes longer. Serve with barley.

PER SERVING (⅙ OF TEMPEH MIXTURE AND ½ CUP BARLEY): 285 grams, 291 Cal, 12 g Total Fat, 2 g Sat Fat, 0 g Trans Fat, 0 mg Chol, 440 mg Sod, 36 g Total Carb, 5 g Total Sugar, 8 g Fib, 15 g Prot, 87 mg Calc.

FYI **Tempeh** is made from fermented soy bean curds. It has a firmer texture than tofu and a slightly nutty, smoky flavor. It is high in protein, cholesterol free, and very low in fat. It is available fresh and frozen. Tempeh can be refrigerated for up to 2 weeks and frozen for up to 3 months.

4

Light Meal or Snack

Beef and Parmesan Bruschetta

LEVEL Basic

PREP 15 min

COOK 10 min

SERVES 6

▲ 1 **(8-ounce) beef tenderloin, trimmed**

1 **teaspoon olive oil**

¼ **teaspoon salt**

¼ **teaspoon black pepper**

▲ ½ **cup lightly packed mixed baby salad greens**

1 **(8-ounce) piece whole grain Italian bread, cut into 12 slices and toasted**

1 **teaspoon white truffle oil or extra-virgin olive oil**

1 **(1-ounce) piece Parmesan cheese, made into shavings with vegetable peeler**

1. Heat large nonstick skillet over medium-high heat. Rub tenderloin with olive oil, salt, and pepper. Place in skillet and cook until browned on all sides and instant-read thermometer inserted into center of beef registers 145°F for medium, about 8 minutes. Transfer to cutting board and let stand 5 minutes. Thinly slice across grain.

2. Divide salad greens evenly among toasts; top evenly with beef. Drizzle evenly with truffle oil and top with Parmesan shavings.

PER SERVING (2 BRUSCHETTA): 72 grams, 182 Cal, 6 g Total Fat, 2 g Sat Fat, 1 g Trans Fat, 22 mg Chol, 418 mg Sod, 21 g Total Carb, 2 g Total Sugar, 2 g Fib, 12 g Prot, 74 mg Calc.

 Truffle oil adds an unexpected rich and exotic flavor to these bruschetta. It is found online and in specialty food stores.

Korean-Style Barbecue Beef

3 PointsPlus© value

Per Serving

LEVEL Basic

PREP 15 min

BROIL 5 min

SERVES 8

½ **cup unseasoned rice vinegar**

¼ **cup reduced-sodium soy sauce**

▲ 1 **small onion, finely chopped**

2 **garlic cloves, minced**

2 **tablespoons brown sugar**

1 **tablespoon grated peeled fresh ginger**

2 **teaspoons fish sauce**

1 **teaspoon chili garlic sauce**

▲ 1¼ **pounds flank steak, trimmed and cut into thin strips**

2 **teaspoons sesame seeds, toasted**

1. Soak 16 (12-inch) wooden skewers in water at least 30 minutes.

2. Meanwhile, to make marinade, combine all ingredients except flank steak and sesame seeds in small bowl.

3. Thread beef evenly onto skewers; place in large baking dish. Pour marinade over beef. Cover and refrigerate, turning skewers occasionally, at least 2 hours or up to 5 hours.

4. Spray broiler rack with nonstick spray. Preheat broiler.

5. Place skewers on broiler rack. Broil 4 inches from heat until beef is browned, about 3 minutes per side. Sprinkle with sesame seeds.

PER SERVING (2 SKEWERS): 79 grams, 128 Cal, 6 g Total Fat, 2 g Sat Fat, 0 g Trans Fat, 30 mg Chol, 477 mg Sod, 5 g Total Carb, 4 g Total Sugar, 0 g Fib, 13 g Prot, 9 mg Calc.

▲ **HEALTHY EXTRA** Serve with a quickly tossed salad of broccoli slaw mix, lemon juice and a pinch of salt and black pepper.

Pork and Scallion Roll-Ups

Pork and Scallion Roll-Ups

3 PointsPlus© value

Per Serving

LEVEL Basic
PREP 15 min
BROIL 5 min
SERVES 6

▲ 1 (¾-pound) lean pork tenderloin, trimmed and cut into 18 slices

1 tablespoon reduced-sodium soy sauce

1 tablespoon oyster sauce

1 tablespoon honey

1 tablespoon Asian (dark) sesame oil

2 teaspoons grated peeled fresh ginger

▲ 18 scallions, cut into 3-inch lengths

1. Place slices of pork between two pieces of plastic wrap. With meat mallet or rolling pin, slightly flatten each slice.

2. To make marinade, stir together soy sauce, oyster sauce, honey, sesame oil, and ginger in large bowl. Add pork and toss to coat. Let stand about 20 minutes.

3. Preheat broiler. Line rack of broiler pan with foil.

4. Wrap 1 slice of pork around each scallion length. Arrange rolls, seam side down, on prepared broiler rack. Broil 5 inches from heat until pork is browned and scallions are just tender, about 5 minutes.

PER SERVING (3 ROLLS): 67 grams, 104 Cal, 4 g Total Fat, 1 g Sat Fat, 0 g Trans Fat, 32 mg Chol, 144 mg Sod, 5 g Total Carb, 3 g Total Sugar, 1 g Fib, 12 g Prot, 15 mg Calc.

 FYI For a more intense flavor, **marinate the pork** in the refrigerator for up to 2 hours.

Shrimp Cakes
with Tarragon Mayonnaise

LEVEL Intermediate

PREP 30 min

COOK 20 min

SERVES 14

▲ 1 **pound cooked shrimp, chopped**

¾ **cup plain dried bread crumbs**

½ **cup fat-free mayonnaise**

▲ 2 **scallions, finely chopped**

4 **teaspoons Dijon mustard**

▲ 1 **large egg white**

▲ ¼ **cup finely chopped unsweetened pickle**

1 **tablespoon chopped fresh tarragon**

1 **tablespoon canola oil**

1. To make shrimp cakes, stir together shrimp, ¼ cup of bread crumbs, ¼ cup of mayonnaise, the scallions, 3 teaspoons of mustard, and the egg white in large bowl. With damp hands, shape mixture into 14 patties.

2. Put remaining ½ cup bread crumbs on sheet of wax paper. Coat patties in crumbs, then transfer to wax paper–lined plate. Cover with plastic wrap and refrigerate until firm, at least 30 minutes or up to 4 hours.

3. Meanwhile, to make tarragon mayonnaise, stir together remaining ¼ cup mayonnaise, the pickle, tarragon, and remaining 1 teaspoon mustard in serving bowl.

4. Heat oil in large nonstick skillet over medium-high heat. Cook patties, in batches, until crisp and golden, about 3 minutes per side. Serve with tarragon mayonnaise.

PER SERVING (1 SHRIMP CAKE AND 2 TEASPOONS MAYONNAISE): 57 grams, 75 Cal, 2 g Total Fat, 0 g Sat Fat, 0 g Trans Fat, 64 mg Chol, 259 mg Sod, 6 g Total Carb, 1 g Total Sugar, 1 g Fib, 8 g Prot, 26 mg Calc.

▲ **HEALTHY EXTRA** Serve these delectable shrimp cakes on a bed of your favorite salad greens accompanied by thick slices of tomato and sweet onion drizzled with balsamic vinegar.

Chicken Satay
with Spicy Peanut Sauce

LEVEL Basic

PREP 20 min

BROIL 10 min

SERVES 8

3   tablespoons creamy peanut butter

2   teaspoons sugar

2   garlic cloves, minced

2   tablespoons reduced-sodium soy sauce

1   tablespoon water

2   teaspoons red wine vinegar

Several drops Sriracha (hot chili sauce)

▲ 2   (5-ounce) skinless boneless chicken breasts, each cut into 6 lengthwise strips

1. Soak 8 (12-inch) wooden skewers in water at least 30 minutes. Line rack of broiler pan with foil and spray with nonstick spray.

2. To make sauce, whisk together peanut butter, sugar, and garlic in small bowl until blended. Add soy sauce, water, vinegar, and Sriracha, whisking until blended. Transfer to serving bowl.

3. Preheat broiler.

4. Thread chicken onto skewers and spray with nonstick spray. Place skewers on rack of broiler pan. Broil 5 inches from heat until cooked through, about 4 minutes per side. Serve with peanut sauce.

PER SERVING (1 SKEWER AND ABOUT 1 TABLESPOON SAUCE): 39 grams, 81 Cal, 4 g Total Fat, 1 g Sat Fat, 0 g Trans Fat, 20 mg Chol, 200 mg Sod, 3 g Total Carb, 2 g Total Sugar, 0 g Fib, 9 g Prot, 7 mg Calc.

Green Curry Seafood

3 PointsPlus value

Per Serving

LEVEL Basic
PREP 20 min
COOK 10 min
SERVES 8

1 **tablespoon canola oil**

3 **shallots, minced**

1 **tablespoon grated peeled fresh ginger**

1 **tablespoon brown sugar**

1 **tablespoon Asian fish sauce**

1 **teaspoon Thai green curry paste**

1 **(14-ounce) can light (low-fat) coconut milk**

▲ 2 **pounds littleneck clams, scrubbed**

▲ 1½ **pounds peeled and deveined large shrimp**

½ **cup coarsely chopped fresh basil**

1. Heat oil in large nonstick Dutch oven over low heat. Add shallots, ginger, brown sugar, fish sauce, and curry paste. Cook, stirring constantly, until fragrant, about 1 minute.

2. Stir coconut milk and clams into pot; increase heat and bring to simmer. Cook, covered, until clams begin to open, about 5 minutes. Stir in shrimp. Cover and cook until clams have opened and shrimp are just opaque in center, about 4 minutes. Discard any clams that do not open. Serve sprinkled with basil.

PER SERVING (ABOUT 2 CUPS): 132 grams, 123 Cal, 5 g Total Fat, 0 g Sat Fat, 0 g Trans Fat, 132 mg Chol, 223 mg Sod, 5 g Total Carb, 1 g Total Sugar, 0 g Fib, 16 g Prot, 39 mg Calc.

▲ **HEALTHY EXTRA** Serve this bold-flavored Thai dish over brown basmati rice (⅔ cup of cooked brown basmati rice with each serving will increase the *PointsPlus* value by *3*).

Green Curry Seafood

Living the Good Health Guidelines

Liquids

▶ **Start your meal with a bowl of broth.** Besides being a great way to sneak in extra liquids, research suggests that having a broth-based soup as a first course can lead you to consume fewer calories during the rest of the meal.

▶ **Munch on water-rich produce.** Fruits and vegetables have a naturally high water content, so by noshing on grapes, watermelon, tomatoes, cucumber, celery, and bell pepper wedges, you'll boost your water intake.

▶ **Don't rely on thirst.** Thirst is a poor indicator of your hydration status; in fact, some experts say you're already somewhat dehydrated by the time your thirst mechanism kicks in. So it's best to consume fluids regularly throughout the day—before you feel thirsty.

Food Processor White Bean and Tomatillo Dip

2 PointsPlus® value
Per Serving

LEVEL Basic
PREP 15 min
COOK None
SERVES 6

Combine beans and tomatillos in food processor and pulse until chunky puree forms. Transfer bean mixture to serving bowl and stir in remaining ingredients.

▲ **2** (15½-ounce) cans small white beans, rinsed and drained

▲ **1** (12-ounce) can tomatillos, drained and coarsely chopped

▲ **1** (4½-ounce) can chopped mild green chiles, drained

▲ **½** small red onion, finely chopped

½ cup chopped fresh cilantro

3 tablespoons lime juice

2 teaspoons chili powder

¼ teaspoon salt

4 drops hot pepper sauce or to taste

PER SERVING (⅓ CUP): 160 grams, 94 Cal, 1 g Total Fat, 0 g Sat Fat, 0 g Trans Fat, 0 mg Chol, 321 mg Sod, 16 g Total Carb, 1 g Total Sugar, 5 g Fib, 4 g Prot, 34 mg Calc.

▲ **HEALTHY EXTRA** Serve this unusual dip surrounded by Belgian endive leaves.

Chunky Guacamole

Chunky Guacamole

PointsPlus
value

Per Serving

LEVEL Basic

PREP 15 min

COOK None

SERVES 16

2   ripe avocados, halved,
    pitted, and peeled

▲ 1   small jalapeño pepper,
      seeded and minced

▲ ½   small red onion,
      chopped

½   cup chopped fresh
    cilantro

1   tablespoon lime juice

½   teaspoon salt

▲ 4   cups vegetables, such
      as halved baby carrots
      or radishes, asparagus
      lengths, celery sticks,
      and cherry tomatoes

Coarsely mash avocados in serving bowl. Add all remaining ingredients except cut-up vegetables, stirring until mixed well. Serve at once or press a piece of plastic wrap directly onto surface to prevent guacamole from browning. Serve with cut-up vegetables. Can be refrigerated up to 2 hours.

PER SERVING (2 TABLESPOONS): 57 grams, 45 Cal, 3 g Total Fat, 1 g Sat Fat, 0 g Trans Fat, 0 mg Chol, 79 mg Sod, 4 g Total Carb, 1 g Total Sugar, 3 g Fib, 1 g Prot, 7 mg Calc.

FYI There are two types of **avocados**: Hass and Florida (Fuerte). Hass avocados have a dark green pebbly texture that turns almost black when ripe and a rich buttery taste. Florida avocados are much larger with bright green smooth skin and a less intense flavor.

Ricotta, Parmesan, and Sun-Dried Tomato Dip

3
PointsPlus
value
Per Serving

LEVEL Basic

PREP 10 min

COOK None

SERVES 8

▲ 1 **(15-ounce) container fat-free ricotta cheese**

¼ **cup fat-free mayonnaise**

▲ ¼ **cup moist-packed sun-dried tomatoes (not packed in oil), finely chopped**

¼ **cup chopped fresh basil**

2 **tablespoons grated Parmesan cheese**

Pinch cayenne

1 **(8-ounce) piece whole grain French baguette, cut into 16 slices and toasted**

Stir together all ingredients except baguette in serving bowl. Serve with toasts.

PER SERVING (¼ CUP DIP AND 2 TOASTS): 94 grams, 135 Cal, 1 g Total Fat, 0 g Sat Fat, 0 g Trans Fat, 10 mg Chol, 347 mg Sod, 22 g Total Carb, 4 g Total Sugar, 2 g Fib, 8 g Prot, 118 mg Calc.

FYI There are three types of **sun-dried tomatoes** available: moist packed, packed in oil, and dry (which have to be soaked to soften). Moist-packed sun-dried tomatoes are sold in airtight plastic bags, which keep them moist and fresh. They do not contain any oil, which keeps calories low.

Jalapeño Hummus

LEVEL Basic

PREP 5 min

COOK None

SERVES 4

▲ 1   (15½-ounce) can chickpeas, rinsed and drained

2   tablespoons tahini

▲ ½-1 jalapeño pepper, seeded and minced

2   tablespoons lime juice

2   tablespoons water

1   garlic clove, minced

¼   teaspoon salt

2   tablespoons chopped fresh cilantro

Combine all ingredients except cilantro in food processor and pulse until smooth, adding a little water if hummus is too stiff. Transfer to serving bowl and sprinkle with cilantro.

PER SERVING (¼ CUP): 97 grams, 110 Cal, 5 g Total Fat, 1 g Sat Fat, 0 g Trans Fat, 0 mg Chol, 362 mg Sod, 13 g Total Carb, 1 g Total Sugar, 3 g Fib, 5 g Prot, 36 mg Calc.

▲ **HEALTHY EXTRA** Serve this hummus accompanied by dippers, such as broccoli florets, zucchini slices, thickly sliced large white mushrooms, and whole radishes with their leaves attached.

Fruits & Vegetables

▶ **Consume a rainbow a day.** To meet (or exceed) your daily quota of fruits and veggies and to maximize the nutritional benefits from your choices, choose a different color with each selection: red (red bell peppers, tomatoes, apples), orange (carrots, oranges, cantaloupe), yellow (summer squash, corn, peaches), green (spinach, kale, broccoli, grapes), blue or purple (eggplant, red cabbage, blueberries, grapes), white (onions, leeks, turnips, honeydew melon), and so on.

▶ **Snack on veggies.** Carrot, celery, and zucchini sticks are excellent (nutrient- and fiber-rich) finger foods to munch on between meals. Prepare a batch ahead of time and keep them in the fridge to snack on when the urge strikes.

▶ **Put out a fruit bowl.** Whether you set the bowl on your kitchen table or on the counter, having fresh fruit—apples, bananas, oranges, pears—within easy reach will encourage everyone in your family to grab a healthy snack. This strategy is the opposite of out of sight, out of mind: By keeping healthy choices in your field of vision, you'll be more likely to gravitate toward them.

Classic Deviled Eggs

3
PointsPlus®
value
Per Serving

LEVEL Basic

PREP 15 min

COOK 5 min

SERVES 6

▲ **6   large eggs**

**3   tablespoons fat-free
    mayonnaise**

**½   teaspoon mustard
    powder**

**½   teaspoon white wine
    vinegar**

¼   teaspoon black pepper

⅛   teaspoon salt

Paprika

1. Place eggs in medium saucepan with enough water to cover by at least 1 inch; bring to boil. Immediately remove saucepan from heat. Let stand, covered, 15 minutes. Pour off water; rinse eggs under cold running water to cool.

2. Peel eggs; cut lengthwise in half and remove yolks. Transfer yolks to small bowl and mash with fork until smooth. Add all remaining ingredients except paprika, stirring to mix well.

3. Place egg whites on platter. Spoon yolk mixture evenly into egg white halves or spoon yolk mixture into pastry bag fitted with star tip and pipe into egg white halves. Sprinkle with paprika and serve at once or loosely cover and refrigerate up to 4 hours.

PER SERVING (2 DEVILED EGGS): 58 grams, 85 Cal, 6 g Total Fat, 2 g Sat Fat, 0 g Trans Fat, 213 mg Chol, 171 mg Sod, 2 g Total Carb, 1 g Total Sugar, 0 g Fib, 6 g Prot, 27 mg Calc.

▲ **HEALTHY EXTRA** Stir 1 tablespoon each of finely chopped celery, red bell pepper, and red onion into the yolk mixture in step 2.

Crab Salad–Topped Cucumber

LEVEL Basic
PREP 20 min
COOK None
SERVES 4

▲ ¼ **pound lump crabmeat, picked over**

2 **tablespoons reduced-fat mayonnaise**

▲ 1 **tablespoon finely chopped celery**

1 **tablespoon finely chopped chives**

2 **teaspoons lime juice**

Pinch cayenne

▲ 20 **thick cucumber slices**

Combine all ingredients except cucumber in medium bowl. Spoon about 1 teaspoon of crab mixture onto each cucumber slice. Arrange on platter and serve at once or cover and refrigerate up to 2 hours.

PER SERVING (5 CRAB-TOPPED CUCUMBER SLICES):
76 grams, 51 Cal, 5 g Total Fat, 0 g Sat Fat, 0 g Trans Fat, 19 mg Chol, 222 mg Sod, 2 g Total Carb, 0 g Total Sugar, 0 g Fib, 4 g Prot, 99 mg Calc.

FYI **Blue crabs,** found along the eastern seaboard and Gulf coast, are prized for their lump crabmeat. These succulent chunks of crab, which are taken from the body, are appreciated for their taste and texture. Be sure to buy crabmeat from a fish store with a good turnover, and pick it over for pieces of shell and cartilage.

Crab Salad-Topped Cucumber

Black Bean and Mushroom Quesadillas

LEVEL Basic

PREP 15 min

COOK 10 min

SERVES 6

▲ 6 ounces white mushrooms, sliced

▲ 1 cup rinsed and drained canned black beans

▲ 1 small tomato, chopped

▲ 2 scallions, thinly sliced

½ cup shredded reduced-fat pepper Jack cheese

4 (7-inch) fat-free whole wheat tortillas

▲ ⅓ cup fat-free sour cream

1. Spray large nonstick skillet with nonstick spray and set over medium heat. Add mushrooms and cook, stirring, until mushrooms release their juice and it is evaporated, about 8 minutes. Transfer to plate and let cool slightly. Wipe skillet clean.

2. Layer one-fourth each of mushrooms, beans, tomato, scallions, and pepper Jack on half of each tortilla. Fold unfilled half of each tortilla over filling, pressing down lightly.

3. Spray skillet with nonstick spray and set over medium-high heat. Place 2 quesadillas in skillet and cook until browned in spots, about 3 minutes. Spray quesadillas with nonstick spray and turn over. Cook until quesadillas are browned in spots and filling is heated through, about 2 minutes longer. Transfer to cutting board; keep warm. Repeat with remaining 2 quesadillas. Cut each quesadilla into 3 wedges and serve with sour cream.

PER SERVING (2 WEDGES AND SCANT 1 TABLESPOON SOUR CREAM): 148 grams, 155 Cal, 4 g Total Fat, 1 g Sat Fat, 0 g Trans Fat, 7 mg Chol, 267 mg Sod, 25 g Total Carb, 2 g Total Sugar, 4 g Fib, 8 g Prot, 165 mg Calc.

▲ **HEALTHY EXTRA** Accompany these tempting quesadillas with fat-free tomato or tomatillo salsa.

New York Deli–Style Quesadillas

LEVEL Basic
PREP 15 min
COOK 10 min
SERVES 4

¼ cup fat-free Thousand Island dressing

2 (7-inch) fat-free whole wheat tortillas

▲ 1 (¼-pound) piece skinless roasted turkey breast, shredded

▲ 1 cup tightly packed coleslaw mix

½ cup shredded reduced-fat low-sodium Swiss cheese

1. Spread dressing evenly over half of each tortilla. Layer one-fourth each of turkey, coleslaw, and Swiss over dressing. Fold unfilled half of each tortilla over filling, pressing down lightly.

2. Spray large skillet with nonstick spray and set over medium-high heat. Place 2 quesadillas in skillet and cook until browned in spots, about 3 minutes. Spray quesadillas with nonstick spray and turn over. Cook until bottoms of quesadillas are browned in spots and filling is heated through, about 2 minutes longer. Transfer to cutting board; keep warm. Repeat with remaining quesadillas. Cut each quesadilla in half.

PER SERVING (2 WEDGES): 101 grams, 159 Cal, 5 g Total Fat, 2 g Sat Fat, 0 g Trans Fat, 25 mg Chol, 244 mg Sod, 17 g Total Carb, 4 g Total Sugar, 2 g Fib, 12 g Prot, 182 mg Calc.

▲ **HEALTHY EXTRA** Serve spears of unsweetened pickles alongside the quesadillas for an authentic deli experience.

Provençal Tomato Tart

Provençal Tomato Tart

LEVEL Intermediate

PREP 20 min

BAKE 20 min

SERVES 12

▲ **5** large plum tomatoes, thinly sliced

▲ **1** onion, very thinly sliced

12 pitted Kalamata olives, quartered

2 teaspoons herbes de Provence

8 (12 x 17-inch) sheets frozen phyllo dough, thawed

½ cup grated Parmesan cheese

1. Place tomato slices between sheets of paper towels and pat dry. Let stand 10 minutes. Mix together onion, olives, and herbes de Provence in small bowl.

2. Preheat oven to 400°F. Spray baking sheet with nonstick spray.

3. Lay 1 sheet of phyllo on baking sheet; lightly spray with olive oil nonstick spray. (Keep remaining phyllo covered with damp paper towel and plastic wrap to keep it from drying out.). Repeat layering with remaining phyllo, spraying each sheet with nonstick spray. Roll edges of phyllo in to form rim.

4. Arrange tomato slices on phyllo in single layer; top with onion mixture. Lightly spray with nonstick spray. Bake until edges of phyllo are golden brown and tomatoes and onion are softened, about 20 minutes. Sprinkle with Parmesan. Cut tart into 12 equal pieces. Serve hot, warm, or at room temperature.

PER SERVING (1 PIECE): 54 grams, 64 Cal, 2 g Total Fat, 1 g Sat Fat, 0 g Trans Fat, 3 mg Chol, 199 mg Sod, 9 g Total Carb, 1 g Total Sugar, 1 g Fib, 3 g Prot, 55 mg Calc.

FYI **Herbes de Provence** are a mix of dried herbs that are grown in the south of France. Packed into decorative red clay crocks, they are available in some supermarkets and in specialty food stores. Herbes de Provence usually includes basil, fennel, lavender, marjoram, rosemary, sage, and thyme. It is a very fragrant blend, so a little goes a long way.

Caramelized Onion–Feta Squares

3
PointsPlus
value

Per Serving

LEVEL Intermediate
PREP 15 min
COOK/BAKE 45 min
SERVES 12

2   teaspoons olive oil
▲ 3   onions, thinly sliced
1   teaspoon sugar
½   teaspoon salt
¼   teaspoon black pepper
1   (16-ounce) refrigerated whole wheat pizza dough, at room temperature
4   ounces reduced-fat feta cheese, crumbled
1   teaspoon dried thyme

1. Heat oil in large nonstick skillet over low heat. Add onions; sprinkle with sugar, salt, and pepper. Cook, stirring, until onions are softened and golden brown, about 25 minutes, adding a little water if onions seem dry. Remove skillet from heat; let cool slightly.

2. Set rack on lowest rung of oven. Preheat oven to 450°F. Spray 10½ x 15½-inch jelly-roll pan with olive oil nonstick spray.

3. With floured hands, stretch and press pizza dough into prepared pan. Spread onion mixture over dough; sprinkle with feta and thyme.

4. Bake until crust is nicely browned and cheese is softened, about 20 minutes. Cut into 12 equal pieces.

PER SERVING (1 PIECE): 78 grams, 126 Cal, 3 g Total Fat, 1 g Sat Fat, 0 g Trans Fat, 3 mg Chol, 221 mg Sod, 20 g Total Carb, 2 g Total Sugar, 3 g Fib, 5 g Prot, 39 mg Calc.

FYI To make the **pizza dough** easier to work with, allow it to stand (covered) at room temperature for about 15 minutes. This short resting time will enable the dough to relax, making it easier to stretch in the pan.

Oven-Roasted Eggplant–Bell Pepper Bruschetta

LEVEL Basic

PREP 15 min

ROAST 45 min

SERVES 12

▲ 1 **(1-pound) eggplant, cut into ½-inch pieces**

▲ 2 **red bell peppers, chopped**

▲ 2 **zucchini, thinly sliced**

1 **tablespoon extra-virgin olive oil**

½ **teaspoon salt**

¼ **teaspoon black pepper**

1 **(8-ounce) piece French baguette, cut into 24 slices and toasted**

¼ **cup lightly packed thinly sliced fresh basil**

2 **tablespoons grated Romano cheese**

1. Preheat oven to 425°F.

2. Toss together eggplant, bell peppers, zucchini, oil, salt, and black pepper in large shallow roasting pan. Spread to form single layer. Roast, stirring occasionally, until vegetables are tender and lightly browned, about 45 minutes.

3. Spoon vegetable mixture evenly onto toasts. Sprinkle evenly with basil and Romano.

PER SERVING (2 BRUSCHETTA): 110 grams, 115 Cal, 4 g Total Fat, 1 g Sat Fat, 0 g Trans Fat, 1 mg Chol, 226 mg Sod, 19 g Total Carb, 3 g Total Sugar, 3 g Fib, 3 g Prot, 26 mg Calc.

FYI **Romano cheese**, which gets its name from the city of Rome, is a sharp-tasting, tangy cheese. The best-known type of Romano is Pecorino-Romano, which is made from sheep's milk.

Escarole Salad Pizza

LEVEL Basic

PREP 20 min

BAKE 10 min

SERVES 4

1 **(10-ounce) prebaked thin whole wheat pizza crust**

2 **tablespoons grated Parmesan cheese**

2 **tablespoons red wine vinegar**

1 **tablespoon extra-virgin olive oil**

½ **teaspoon dried oregano**

¼ **teaspoon black pepper**

▲ 2 **cups lightly packed thinly sliced escarole**

▲ 1 **cup lightly packed thinly sliced radicchio**

▲ 1 **small red bell pepper, thinly sliced**

▲ 1 **small red onion, thinly sliced**

▲ 2 **plum tomatoes, chopped**

▲ 4 **moist-packed sun-dried tomatoes (not packed in oil), chopped**

1. Preheat oven to 400°F.

2. Place pizza crust directly on oven rack; bake until crispy, about 10 minutes.

3. Meanwhile, to make dressing, whisk together Parmesan, vinegar, oil, oregano, and black pepper in large bowl. Add remaining ingredients to dressing; toss to coat evenly. Spoon onto pizza crust. Cut into 4 wedges.

PER SERVING (1 WEDGE): 179 grams, 257 Cal, 8 g Total Fat, 3 g Sat Fat, 0 g Trans Fat, 2 mg Chol, 449 mg Sod, 41 g Total Carb, 5 g Total Sugar, 9 g Fib, 11 g Prot, 135 mg Calc.

Escarole Salad Pizza

Chickpea-Goat Cheese Toasts

LEVEL Basic

PREP 15 min

ROAST 20 min

SERVES 6

▲ 1 **(15½-ounce) can chickpeas, rinsed and drained**

2 **garlic cloves, minced**

1 **teaspoon ground cumin**

1 **teaspoon olive oil**

▲ 1 **tomato, chopped**

¼ **teaspoon salt**

⅛ **teaspoon black pepper**

3 **(6-inch) whole wheat pita breads, each cut into 4 wedges**

1 **ounce soft goat cheese, crumbled**

1. Preheat oven to 400°F.

2. Mix together chickpeas, garlic, cumin, and oil in 8-inch square baking dish. Roast, stirring occasionally, 15 minutes. Transfer chickpeas to medium bowl; stir in tomato, salt, and pepper.

3. Arrange pita bread wedges on baking sheet. Bake until crisp, about 5 minutes.

4. Spoon chickpea mixture evenly onto pita wedges; sprinkle evenly with goat cheese. Serve warm.

PER SERVING (2 TOASTS): 111 grams, 154 Cal, 3 g Total Fat, 1 g Sat Fat, 0 g Trans Fat, 2 mg Chol, 430 mg Sod, 26 g Total Carb, 2 g Total Sugar, 5 g Fib, 7 g Prot, 33 mg Calc.

 FYI **Mash chickpeas slightly** after baking to help prevent them from rolling off the toasted pita wedges.

Nachos Pizzeria Style

3 PointsPlus value

Per Serving

LEVEL Basic

PREP 15 min

BROIL 1 min

SERVES 4

24 **baked tortilla chips**

½ **cup fat-free marinara sauce**

▲ 24 **slices white mushrooms**

½ **cup shredded part-skim mozzarella cheese**

½ **teaspoon dried oregano**

½ **teaspoon dried basil**

1. Preheat broiler.

2. Place tortilla chips in jelly-roll pan in single layer. Spoon 1 teaspoon marinara sauce on each chip; top each with mushroom slice and 1 teaspoon mozzarella. Sprinkle evenly with oregano and basil. Broil until cheese begins to melt, about 1 minute.

PER SERVING (6 NACHOS): 59 grams, 108 Cal, 3 g Total Fat, 2 g Sat Fat, 0 g Trans Fat, 8 mg Chol, 221 mg Sod, 15 g Total Carb, 3 g Total Sugar, 2 g Fib, 5 g Prot, 137 mg Calc.

▲ **HEALTHY EXTRA** Top each nacho with one or two thin zucchini slices along with the mushrooms.

Curried Fruit and Nut Popcorn
and Nachos Pizzeria Style, page 157

Curried Fruit and Nut Popcorn

LEVEL Basic

PREP 5 min

MICROWAVE 1 min

SERVES 8

1   tablespoon olive oil

2   teaspoons curry powder

▲ 6   cups plain air-popped popcorn

½   cup finely chopped dried apricots

⅓   cup pistachio nuts, chopped

1. Stir together oil and curry powder in microwavable cup. Microwave on High until fragrant, about 1 minute.

2. Toss together remaining ingredients in large bowl. Drizzle curry oil over popcorn and toss to coat evenly.

PER SERVING (¾ CUP): 29 grams, 83 Cal, 5 g Total Fat, 1 g Sat Fat, 0 g Trans Fat, 0 mg Chol, 22 mg Sod, 10 g Total Carb, 3 g Total Sugar, 2 g Fib, 2 g Prot, 11 mg Calc.

Spicy Garlic and Onion Pita Chips

LEVEL Basic

PREP 15 min

BAKE 10 min

SERVES 8

4 (6-inch) oat bran pita breads

▲ 2 large egg whites

3 garlic cloves, minced

1 teaspoon onion powder

¼ teaspoon salt

¼ teaspoon cayenne or to taste

3 tablespoons grated Parmesan cheese

1. Preheat oven to 350°F.

2. Split each pita in half to make 8 rounds total; cut each round into 6 wedges. Arrange wedges, smooth side down, on one or two baking sheets.

3. Beat egg whites, garlic, onion powder, salt, and cayenne in small bowl until frothy. Brush over pita wedges; sprinkle evenly with Parmesan.

4. Bake until edges of pita chips are browned and topping is set, about 10 minutes. Transfer chips to racks and let cool completely.

PER SERVING (6 CHIPS): 30 grams, 46 Cal, 2 g Total Fat, 0 g Sat Fat, 0 g Trans Fat, 2 mg Chol, 272 mg Sod, 5 g Total Carb, 0 g Total Sugar, 2 g Fib, 5 g Prot, 29 mg Calc.

 FYI These tasty **pita chips** can be stored in an airtight container for up to 5 days.

Sugar and Spice Popcorn

PointsPlus®
value
Per Serving

LEVEL Basic

PREP 10 min

COOK None

SERVES 8

▲ 8 cups plain air-popped
popcorn

2 tablespoons superfine
sugar

2 teaspoons ground
cinnamon

¼ teaspoon ground
allspice

¼ teaspoon ground cloves

¼ teaspoon ground ginger

¼ teaspoon ground
nutmeg

1. Put popcorn in very large bowl. Lightly spray with nonstick spray, tossing constantly while spraying.

2. Mix together remaining ingredients in cup. Gradually sprinkle over popcorn, tossing to coat evenly.

PER SERVING (1 CUP): 96 grams, 45 Cal, 0 g Total Fat, 0 g Sat Fat, 0 g Trans Fat, 0 mg Chol, 1 mg Sod, 10 g Total Carb, 3 g Total Sugar, 2 g Fib, 1 g Prot, 9 mg Calc.

FYI Here's how to **turn regular sugar into superfine sugar:** Put the sugar into a blender or food processor and process until fine. It's quick and costs less than store-bought superfine sugar.

Mini Banana-Walnut Parfaits

LEVEL Basic

PREP 15 min

COOK None

SERVES 4

Layer one-fourth of cookies, frozen yogurt, walnuts, banana, and fudge topping in each of 4 small wine glasses. Top each with 1 strawberry.

4   vanilla wafer cookies, coarsely crushed

1   cup chocolate fat-free frozen yogurt

2   tablespoons chopped walnuts

▲ 1   small banana, cut into 12 slices

2   tablespoons fat-free hot fudge topping

▲ 4   small strawberries with stems

PER SERVING (1 PARFAIT): 87 grams, 136 Cal, 4 g Total Fat, 1 g Sat Fat, 0 g Trans Fat, 1 mg Chol, 61 mg Sod, 25 g Total Carb, 17 g Total Sugar, 2 g Fib, 4 g Prot, 99 mg Calc.

FYI If you have the time, **toast the walnuts**, as it brings out their nutty flavor and crisps them. Here's how: Place the nuts in a small dry skillet over medium-low heat. Cook, shaking the pan often, until the nuts are lightly browned and fragrant, about 4 minutes. Transfer to a plate to cool.

Chocolate-Orange Mousse

LEVEL Intermediate

PREP 5 min

COOK 10 min

SERVES 8

4 ounces semisweet chocolate, chopped

1½ tablespoons orange liqueur

1 tablespoon light corn syrup

⅓ cup warm water

▲ **2 tablespoons powdered egg whites**

¼ cup sugar

1. Fill small saucepan with 1 inch of water and bring to simmer over medium heat. Put chocolate in small bowl and set over simmering water. Cook, stirring, until chocolate is melted and smooth, about 5 minutes. Remove bowl from saucepan.

2. Combine chocolate, liqueur, and corn syrup in medium bowl. Whisk together powdered egg whites and warm water until egg white powder is completely dissolved, about 2 minutes. With electric mixer on low speed, beat egg white mixture until foamy. Increase speed to medium-high and beat until soft peaks form when beaters are lifted. Add sugar, 1 tablespoon at a time, beating until stiff, glossy peaks form when beaters are lifted.

3. With rubber spatula, stir about one-third of meringue into chocolate mixture to lighten it. Fold remaining meringue into chocolate mixture in two batches just until whites are no longer visible. Spoon mousse into serving bowl. Refrigerate, covered, until firm, at least 3 hours or up to overnight.

PER SERVING (⅛ OF MOUSSE): 38 grams, 118 Cal, 6 g Total Fat, 3 g Sat Fat, 0 g Trans Fat, 0 mg Chol, 25 mg Sod, 17 g Total Carb, 14 g Total Sugar, 1 g Fib, 2 g Prot, 0 g Alcohol, 0 g Sugar Alcohol, 2 mg Calc.

Grilled Nectarines with Raspberry Sorbet and Berries

5 PointsPlus value
Per Serving

LEVEL Basic

PREP 15 min

GRILL 5 min

SERVES 4

▲ **4 large nectarines, halved and pitted**

1½ tablespoons sugar

1 pint raspberry sorbet, slightly softened

▲ **1 (6-ounce) container raspberries**

4 fresh mint sprigs

1. Preheat grill to medium or prepare medium fire using direct method.

2. Spray cut sides of nectarines with olive oil nonstick spray and sprinkle evenly with sugar. Place nectarines, cut side down, on grill rack and grill, turning once, until slightly softened and nicely marked, about 3 minutes per side. Transfer to plate.

3. Place 2 nectarine halves on each of 4 plates. Place ¼-cup scoop of sorbet in each half. Scatter raspberries around nectarines and garnish each serving with mint sprig.

PER SERVING (1 DESSERT): 319 grams, 207 Cal, 1 g Total Fat, 0 g Sat Fat, 0 g Trans Fat, 0 mg Chol, 5 mg Sod, 49 g Total Carb, 41 g Total Sugar, 5 g Fib, 3 g Prot, 17 mg Calc.

FYI The nectarines can also be cooked in a grill pan or broiled.

Don't Eat Out, Eat In

Pork Lo Mein

Pork Lo Mein

7 PointsPlus® value
Per Serving

LEVEL Basic
PREP 20 min
COOK 30 min
SERVES 6

▲ ½ **pound whole wheat spaghetti**

▲ 1 **cup reduced-sodium chicken broth**

2 **tablespoons dry sherry**

2 **tablespoons reduced-sodium soy sauce**

1½ **tablespoons cornstarch**

1 **teaspoon Asian (dark) sesame oil**

▲ ¾ **pound lean pork tenderloin, cut into thin strips**

▲ ½ **pound shiitake mushrooms, stemmed and caps sliced**

▲ 3 **scallions, sliced**

3 **garlic cloves, finely chopped**

1. Cook spaghetti according to package directions, omitting salt if desired; drain in colander. Rinse under cold running water; drain again. Transfer to medium bowl.

2. Meanwhile, whisk together broth, sherry, soy sauce, cornstarch, and sesame oil in small bowl until smooth.

3. Spray nonstick wok or large deep skillet with nonstick spray and set over high heat. Add pork and stir-fry until browned, about 4 minutes; transfer to plate.

4. Spray wok with nonstick spray. Add mushrooms, scallions, and garlic; stir-fry until mushrooms are softened, about 3 minutes. Re-stir broth mixture; add to wok and stir-fry until sauce bubbles and thickens, about 2 minutes. Stir in pork and spaghetti. Stir-fry until heated through, about 1 minute longer.

PER SERVING (1 CUP): 179 grams, 264 Cal, 4 g Total Fat, 1 g Sat Fat, 0 g Trans Fat, 38 mg Chol, 234 mg Sod, 38 g Total Carb, 3 g Total Sugar, 6 g Fib, 20 g Prot, 29 mg Calc.

FYI Because **stir-frying** requires high heat, it's best to use canola or vegetable nonstick spray (olive oil spray will start to smoke too quickly).

Living the Good Health Guidelines

Sodium, Sugar & Alcohol

▶ **Read the labels.** Most of the sodium in the diet of most Americans comes from processed foods and restaurant foods. So get in the habit of perusing the labels on packaged foods—the lower the sodium content, the better. Look for products that are labeled "low sodium," "reduced sodium," "light in sodium," "sodium-free," or "unsalted." And ask to have your restaurant meals prepared with a minimum of salt.

▶ **Budget for sweets.** There's nothing wrong with having a small sweet treat every day, but you need to account for it by adjusting the other food you eat or your portion sizes. If you prefer, you can save the calories from a daily treat and allow yourself one rich dessert a week instead.

▶ **Make your first cocktail sparkling water.** Whether you're at a party or a bar, start with club soda or sparkling water and hold the glass in your dominant hand to make nibbling a greater challenge. You'll hydrate yourself before drinking alcohol, and you'll give yourself time to settle into the scene before enjoying a cocktail.

Kung Pao Chicken

6 PointsPlus value
Per Serving

LEVEL Basic

PREP 20 min

COOK 10 min

SERVES 4

▲ ¾ **cup reduced-sodium chicken broth**

¼ **cup rice wine**

2 **tablespoons reduced-sodium soy sauce**

1 **tablespoon honey**

1 **tablespoon cornstarch**

2 **teaspoons chili garlic sauce**

1½ **teaspoons canola oil**

▲ 1 **pound chicken tenders, cut into 1-inch chunks**

▲ ½ **small red onion, chopped**

2 **teaspoons grated peeled fresh ginger**

▲ 4 **cups small broccoli florets**

▲ 1 **(8-ounce) can sliced water chestnuts, drained**

1. Whisk together broth, rice wine, soy sauce, honey, cornstarch, and chili garlic sauce in small bowl until smooth.

2. Heat nonstick wok or large deep nonstick skillet over high heat until drop of water sizzles in pan; add oil and swirl to coat pan. Add chicken and stir-fry until cooked through, about 3 minutes; transfer to plate.

3. Reduce heat to medium-high; spray wok with nonstick spray. Add onion and ginger; stir-fry until fragrant, about 30 seconds. Add broccoli and water chestnuts; stir-fry until broccoli is crisp-tender, about 2 minutes. Re-stir cornstarch mixture; add to wok along with chicken. Stir-fry until sauce bubbles and thickens, about 2 minutes longer.

PER SERVING (1¼ CUPS): 291 grams, 242 Cal, 5 g Total Fat, 1 g Sat Fat, 0 g Trans Fat, 63 mg Chol, 436 mg Sod, 19 g Total Carb, 6 g Total Sugar, 4 g Fib, 27 g Prot, 55 mg Calc.

▲ **HEALTHY EXTRA** Add 4 scallions cut into 2-inch lengths to the wok along with the broccoli in step 3.

Szechuan Turkey

5
PointsPlus©
value
Per Serving

LEVEL Basic
PREP 15 min
COOK 10 min
SERVES 4

▲ 1   **pound turkey cutlets, cut into thin strips**

3   **tablespoons hoisin sauce**

2   **tablespoons cornstarch**

▲ ½   **cup reduced-sodium chicken broth**

1   **tablespoon white wine vinegar**

2   **teaspoons chili garlic sauce**

1½   **teaspoons canola oil**

2   **garlic cloves, minced**

1½   **teaspoons grated peeled fresh ginger**

▲ 1   **yellow bell pepper, diced**

▲ 2   **carrots, thinly sliced**

1. Stir together turkey, 1 tablespoon of hoisin sauce, and 1 tablespoon of cornstarch in medium bowl until coated evenly.

2. Whisk together remaining 2 tablespoons hoisin sauce, remaining 1 tablespoon cornstarch, the broth, vinegar, and chili garlic sauce in small bowl until blended.

3. Heat nonstick wok or large deep skillet over high heat until drop of water sizzles in pan; add oil and swirl to coat pan. Add turkey mixture and stir-fry until turkey is almost cooked through, about 2 minutes. Add garlic and ginger; stir-fry until fragrant, about 30 seconds. Add bell pepper and carrots; stir-fry until crisp-tender, about 2 minutes. Re-stir cornstarch mixture; add to wok and stir-fry until sauce bubbles and thickens and turkey is cooked through, about 2 minutes longer.

PER SERVING (1 CUP): 247 grams, 210 Cal, 3 g Total Fat, 0 g Sat Fat, 0 g Trans Fat, 45 mg Chol, 466 mg Sod, 16 g Total Carb, 7 g Total Sugar, 2 g Fib, 30 g Prot, 24 mg Calc.

▲ **HEALTHY EXTRA** Serve a bowl of brown rice alongside this Szechuan-style stir-fry (²/₃ cup of cooked brown rice with each serving will increase the *PointsPlus* value by *3*).

Shrimp with Black Bean Sauce

LEVEL Basic

PREP 15 min

COOK 10 min

SERVES 4

▲ 1 **pound large shrimp, peeled and deveined, tails left on if desired**

2 **tablespoons cornstarch**

▲ ½ **cup reduced-sodium chicken broth**

2 **tablespoons black bean sauce**

1 **tablespoon reduced-sodium soy sauce**

1 **teaspoon Asian (dark) sesame oil**

1 **shallot, finely chopped**

1½ **teaspoons grated peeled fresh ginger**

▲ ¼ **pound white or cremini mushrooms, quartered**

▲ ¼ **pound snow peas, trimmed and halved**

▲ 1 **small yellow bell pepper, thinly sliced**

▲ 1 **carrot, thinly sliced**

1. Toss together shrimp and 1 tablespoon of cornstarch in medium bowl until coated evenly.

2. Whisk together broth, black bean sauce, soy sauce, and remaining 1 tablespoon cornstarch in small bowl until smooth.

3. Heat nonstick wok or large deep nonstick skillet over high heat until drop of water sizzles in pan; add sesame oil and swirl to coat pan. Add shrimp and stir-fry until just opaque in center, about 2 minutes. Add shallot and ginger; stir-fry until fragrant, about 30 seconds. Add mushrooms, snow peas, bell pepper, and carrot; stir-fry until bell pepper is crisp-tender, about 2 minutes. Re-stir broth mixture; add to wok and stir-fry until sauce bubbles and thickens, about 2 minutes longer.

PER SERVING (1 CUP): 233 grams, 161 Cal, 3 g Total Fat, 1 g Sat Fat, 0 g Trans Fat, 168 mg Chol, 429 mg Sod, 12 g Total Carb, 3 g Total Sugar, 2 g Fib, 21 g Prot, 65 mg Calc.

 FYI To trim fresh snow peas, snap off the stem end from each pod, then pull off the string and discard.

Greek Orzo and Beef Casserole

LEVEL Basic

PREP 20 min

COOK/BAKE 55 min

SERVES 6

▲ 1¼ **cups whole wheat orzo**

▲ 1 **pound ground lean beef (5% fat or less)**

▲ 1 **red onion, chopped**

▲ 2 **celery stalks, chopped**

2 **garlic cloves, minced**

1 **teaspoon dried mint**

½ **teaspoon dried oregano**

▲ 1 **(14½-ounce) can crushed tomatoes in puree**

▲ 2 **tablespoons no-salt added tomato paste**

½ **teaspoon ground cinnamon**

½ **cup crumbled reduced-fat feta cheese**

1 **tablespoon grated Romano cheese**

1. Preheat oven to 350°F. Spray 8-inch square baking dish with nonstick spray.

2. Cook orzo according to package directions, omitting salt if desired; drain in colander. Rinse under cold running water; drain again. Transfer to large bowl.

3. Meanwhile, spray large nonstick skillet with nonstick spray and set over medium-high heat. Add beef and cook, breaking it apart with wooden spoon, until browned, about 4 minutes. Transfer to orzo in bowl.

4. Spray skillet with nonstick spray. Add onion, celery, garlic, mint, and oregano; cook, stirring, until onion is softened, about 5 minutes. Add tomatoes with puree, tomato paste, and cinnamon; reduce heat and simmer until mixture is thickened, about 8 minutes. Stir in feta. Stir into beef mixture. Transfer beef mixture to prepared baking dish; sprinkle with Romano. Bake until heated through, about 25 minutes.

PER SERVING (1 ¼ CUPS): 223 grams, 291 Cal, 7 g Total Fat, 3 g Sat Fat, 0 g Trans Fat, 50 mg Chol, 354 mg Sod, 32 g Total Carb, 4 g Total Sugar, 5 g Fib, 25 g Prot, 95 mg Calc.

FYI This dish is equally delicious if you substitute **reduced-fat soft goat cheese** for the feta and grated Parmesan cheese for the Romano.

Greek Orzo and
Beef Casserole

Lamb Shish Kebabs

4 PointsPlus value
Per Servi

LEVEL Basic
PREP 20 min
GRILL 10 min
SERVES 6

2	teaspoons olive oil
2	garlic cloves, minced
1	teaspoon dried oregano
½	teaspoon dried rosemary, crushed
1½	pounds boneless leg of lamb, trimmed and cut into 30 chunks
▲ 2	small red onions, each cut into 6 wedges
▲ 1	large yellow or orange bell pepper, cut into 12 pieces
½	teaspoon salt
¼	teaspoon black pepper

1. Combine oil, garlic, oregano, and rosemary in large zip-close plastic bag; add lamb. Squeeze out air and seal bag; turn to coat lamb. Refrigerate, turning bag occasionally, at least 1 hour or up to overnight.

2. Spray grill rack with nonstick spray. Preheat grill to medium-high or prepare medium-high fire using direct method.

3. Remove lamb from marinade; discard marinade. Alternately thread 5 lamb chunks, 2 onion wedges, and 2 bell pepper pieces onto each of 6 (12-inch) metal skewers. Sprinkle with salt and pepper. Place on prepared grill rack and grill until vegetables are tender and lamb is well marked, about 5 minutes per side for medium.

PER SERVING (1 KEBAB): 117 grams, 182 Cal, 9 g Total Fat, 3 g Sat Fat, 0 g Trans Fat, 74 mg Chol, 254 mg Sod, 4 g Total Carb, 1 g Total Sugar, 1 g Fib, 20 g Prot, 21 mg Calc.

▲ **HEALTHY EXTRA** Serve these kebabs on a bed of whole wheat couscous (⅔ cup of whole wheat couscous with each serving will increase the *PointsPlus* value by *3*).

Lemony Chicken with Potatoes

8 PointsPlus® value
Per Serving

LEVEL Basic

PREP 15 min

ROAST 1 hr

SERVES 4

Juice of 1 lemon

3   garlic cloves, minced

3   teaspoons olive oil

1½ teaspoons dried oregano

½   teaspoon salt

¼   teaspoon black pepper

4   (6-ounce) skinless bone-in chicken thighs, trimmed

▲ 1   pound small potatoes, scrubbed and halved

½   cup water

1. Preheat oven to 425°F. Place rack in large roasting pan.

2. Stir together lemon juice, garlic, 1 teaspoon of oil, the oregano, ¼ teaspoon of salt, and ⅛ teaspoon of pepper in large bowl. Add chicken and toss to coat evenly. Let marinate in refrigerator at least 20 minutes or up to 4 hours.

3. Meanwhile, combine remaining 2 teaspoons oil, ¼ teaspoon salt, and ⅛ teaspoon pepper in medium bowl. Add potatoes and toss to coat evenly. Scatter potatoes around rack in roasting pan; roast 20 minutes.

4. Remove chicken from marinade; reserve marinade. Place chicken on rack. Stir water into marinade; pour over chicken and potatoes. Roast until potatoes are tender and instant-read thermometer inserted into thickest part of thigh (not touching bone) registers 165°F, about 40 minutes, basting with pan juices halfway through roasting time.

PER SERVING (1 CHICKEN THIGH AND ¼ OF POTATOES): 228 grams, 309 Cal, 13 g Total Fat, 3 g Sat Fat, 0 g Trans Fat, 86 mg Chol, 381 mg Sod, 21 g Total Carb, 1 g Total Sugar, 2 g Fib, 26 g Prot, 33 mg Calc.

FYI Most supermarkets sell skinned chicken thighs, but it's a better value if you skin them yourself: With a paring knife, make a small slice between the meat and skin to loosen the skin. Grasp the skin with a clean paper towel and pull it away from the meat. Discard the skin and paper towel.

Tandoori-Style
Chicken

Tandoori-Style Chicken

3 PointsPlus⊕ value

Per Serving

LEVEL Basic
PREP 10 min
BROIL 10 min
SERVES 6

▲ ¾ **cup plain fat-free yogurt**

Juice of ½ lemon

1 **tablespoon paprika**

1 **teaspoon grated peeled fresh ginger**

1 **garlic clove, minced**

1 **teaspoon ground cumin**

▲ 6 **(¼-pound) chicken cutlets**

2 **tablespoons chopped fresh cilantro**

1. Combine yogurt, lemon juice, paprika, ginger, garlic, and cumin in large zip-close plastic bag; add chicken. Squeeze out air and seal bag; turn to coat chicken. Refrigerate at least 4 hours or up to overnight.

2. Spray broiler rack with nonstick spray. Preheat broiler.

3. Remove chicken from marinade; discard marinade. Place chicken on prepared broiler rack. Broil chicken 5 inches from heat until cooked through, about 4 minutes per side. Serve sprinkled with cilantro.

PER SERVING (1 CHICKEN CUTLET): 111 grams, 147 Cal, 3 g Total Fat, 1 g Sat Fat, 0 g Trans Fat, 63 mg Chol, 80 mg Sod, 4 g Total Carb, 2 g Total Sugar, 1 g Fib, 25 g Prot, 78 mg Calc.

▲ **HEALTHY EXTRA** Serve this chicken with a sliced cucumber and radish salad sprinkled with dill, lemon juice, and black pepper along with a tablespoon or two of plain fat-free yogurt for each serving.

Fish and Sweet Onion Vindaloo

4 PointsPlus value

Per Serving

LEVEL Basic
PREP 20 min
COOK 20 min
SERVES 6

2 teaspoons canola oil

▲ 1 sweet onion, chopped

2 garlic cloves, minced

2 teaspoons grated peeled fresh ginger

2 teaspoons curry powder

▲ 1½ pounds plum tomatoes, diced

Juice of ½ lemon

½ teaspoon salt

▲ 6 (5-ounce) cod or pollock fillets, skinned

1. Heat oil in large nonstick skillet over medium-high heat. Add onion and cook, stirring, until golden, about 7 minutes. Add garlic, ginger, and curry powder; cook, stirring, until fragrant, about 30 seconds. Stir in tomatoes, lemon juice, and salt; cook, covered, until tomatoes are softened, about 5 minutes.

2. Add cod, skinned side up, to skillet; spoon sauce over fish. Reduce heat and simmer, covered, until fish is just opaque in center, about 8 minutes, basting with sauce halfway through cooking time.

PER SERVING (1 COD FILLET WITH ABOUT ¼ CUP SAUCE): 275 grams, 160 Cal, 3 g Total Fat, 0 g Sat Fat, 0 g Trans Fat, 54 mg Chol, 281 mg Sod, 10 g Total Carb, 6 g Total Sugar, 2 g Fib, 24 g Prot, 42 mg Calc.

FYI If top-quality fresh plum tomatoes are not available, use a 28-ounce can of no-salt added diced tomatoes, drained, in step 1. Cook, uncovered, until the flavors are blended, about 4 minutes.

Vegetable Dal

PointsPlus value

Per Serving

LEVEL Basic
PREP 15 min
COOK 35 min
SERVES 4

▲ 1   **Yukon Gold potato, scrubbed and cut into ½-inch pieces**

▲ ¼   **cup red lentils, picked over, rinsed, and drained**

  1   **tablespoon canola oil**

▲ 1   **red onion, chopped**

▲ 1   **jalapeño pepper, seeded and minced**

  2   **teaspoons curry powder**

▲ 1   **(15½-ounce) can chickpeas, rinsed and drained**

▲ 1   **(14½-ounce) can diced tomatoes**

  2   **garlic cloves, minced**

 1½ **teaspoons grated peeled fresh ginger**

  2   **tablespoons chopped fresh cilantro**

1. Put potato in large saucepan and add enough water to cover; bring to boil. Reduce heat and cook until potato is almost tender, about 7 minutes. With slotted spoon, transfer potato to medium bowl.

2. Add lentils to cooking liquid in saucepan; bring to boil. Reduce heat and cook, uncovered, until lentils are tender but still hold their shape, about 8 minutes; drain.

3. Heat oil in large nonstick skillet over medium-high heat. Add onion, jalapeño, and curry powder. Cook until onion is softened, about 5 minutes. Stir in potato, chickpeas, tomatoes, garlic, and ginger. Cook, stirring occasionally, until potato is tender, about 5 minutes. Stir in lentils and cook until heated through, about 1 minute longer. Remove saucepan from heat and stir in cilantro.

PER SERVING (1 CUP): 351 grams, 263 Cal, 5 g Total Fat, 0 g Sat Fat, 0 g Trans Fat, 0 mg Chol, 474 mg Sod, 45 g Total Carb, 8 g Total Sugar, 9 g Fib, 10 g Prot, 60 mg Calc.

 FYI **If the dal is a bit too thick,** stir in a little reduced-sodium vegetable broth or water until the desired consistency.

Pork Piccata

PointsPlus value
Per Servin

LEVEL Basic
PREP 10 min
COOK 10 min
SERVES 4

½ **cup Italian-seasoned dried bread crumbs**

▲ ¼ **cup fat-free egg substitute**

2 **tablespoons whole grain mustard**

▲ 4 **(¼-pound) boneless lean pork loin chops, trimmed and pounded to ¼-inch thickness**

2 **teaspoons extra-virgin olive oil**

▲ 2 **tablespoons reduced-sodium chicken broth**

Juice of ½ lemon

1 **tablespoon finely chopped fresh parsley**

1. Spread bread crumbs on sheet of wax paper. Beat egg substitute and mustard in large shallow bowl or pie plate. Working with 1 piece of pork at a time, dip into egg mixture, then coat with bread crumbs, pressing lightly so they adhere. Transfer to large plate.

2. Heat oil in large nonstick skillet over medium heat. Add pork and cook until golden and cooked through, about 5 minutes per side. Transfer pork to platter; keep warm.

3. To make sauce, whisk broth and lemon juice into skillet; simmer 30 seconds. Stir in parsley. Pour sauce over pork.

PER SERVING (1 PORK CUTLET WITH ABOUT 1 TABLESPOON SAUCE): 132 grams, 225 Cal, 9 g Total Fat, 2 g Sat Fat, 0 g Trans Fat, 66 mg Chol, 320 mg Sod, 11 g Total Carb, 1 g Total Sugar, 1 g Fib, 25 g Prot, 46 mg Calc.

FYI **Pounding the pork to an even thickness** ensures that the meat cooks uniformly. The easiest way to do this is to place the pork between two pieces of plastic wrap, leaving room around each chop. Then, with a meat mallet, rolling pin, or bottom of a small heavy saucepan, pound the meat to the desired thickness.

Risotto with Sausage and Greens

LEVEL Intermediate

PREP 15 min

COOK 40 min

SERVES 6

½ **pound sweet Italian-style chicken sausage, casings removed and sausage broken up**

▲ ½ **bunch broccoli rabe, trimmed and chopped**

▲ 3 **cups reduced-sodium chicken broth**

2 **teaspoons extra-virgin olive oil**

2 **shallots, minced**

1¼ **cups Arborio or other short-grain white rice**

⅓ **cup dry vermouth**

¼ **teaspoon black pepper**

1. Spray large nonstick skillet with nonstick spray and set over medium heat. Add sausage and cook, stirring occasionally, until lightly browned, about 5 minutes. Stir in broccoli rabe; cook, covered, until broccoli rabe is tender and sausage is cooked through, about 7 minutes. Remove skillet from heat.

2. Meanwhile, bring broth to boil in medium saucepan. Reduce heat and keep at gentle simmer.

3. Heat oil in nonstick Dutch oven over medium heat. Add shallots and cook, stirring occasionally, until softened, about 3 minutes. Add rice and cook, stirring frequently, until lightly toasted, about 3 minutes. Add vermouth and cook, stirring frequently, until almost absorbed, about 1 minute. Add simmering broth, ½ cup at a time, stirring until broth is absorbed before adding more; cook until rice is tender but still chewy in center. Add sausage mixture and pepper; cook, stirring frequently, just until heated through, about 1 minute longer.

PER SERVING (1 CUP): 262 grams, 253 Cal, 5 g Total Fat, 1 g Sat Fat, 0 g Trans Fat, 29 mg Chol, 492 mg Sod, 36 g Total Carb, 1 g Total Sugar, 2 g Fib, 13 g Prot, 31 mg Calc.

▲ **HEALTHY EXTRA** Start your meal with a tasty sliced mushroom and baby arugula salad dressed with lemon juice.

Lasagna Bolognese

LEVEL Intermediate

PREP 25 min

COOK/BAKE 1 hr 10 min

SERVES 6

▲ 9 **whole wheat lasagna noodles**

▲ ½ **pound ground skinless turkey breast**

▲ 1 **onion, chopped**

▲ 1 **orange or yellow bell pepper, diced**

▲ 1 **zucchini, diced**

1 **teaspoon fennel seeds, finely crushed**

▲ 2 **(16-ounce) jars fat-free marinara sauce**

▲ 1½ **cups fat-free ricotta cheese**

¾ **cup shredded low-fat Italian cheese blend**

1. Preheat oven to 375°F. Spray 9 x13-inch baking dish with nonstick spray.

2. Cook noodles according to package directions, omitting salt if desired; drain in colander. Rinse under cold running water; drain again.

3. Meanwhile, to make sauce, spray large nonstick skillet with nonstick spray and set over medium-high heat. Add turkey, onion, bell pepper, zucchini, and fennel seeds. Cook, breaking turkey apart with wooden spoon, until browned and pan juices are evaporated, about 10 minutes.

4. Stir marinara sauce into skillet and bring to boil. Reduce heat and simmer until sauce is slightly thickened and flavors are blended, about 10 minutes.

5. Spread one-fourth of sauce in prepared baking dish. Top with 3 noodles; spread ½ cup of ricotta over noodles. Repeat layering with sauce, noodles, and ricotta two times; top with remaining sauce. Cover dish with foil and bake 30 minutes. Uncover and sprinkle cheese blend over lasagna. Bake, uncovered, until heated through and cheeses are lightly browned, about 20 minutes longer. Let stand 10 minutes before serving.

PER SERVING (⅙ OF LASAGNA): 393 grams, 355 Cal, 3 g Total Fat, 1 g Sat Fat, 0 g Trans Fat, 23 mg Chol, 837 mg Sod, 49 g Total Carb, 6 g Total Sugar, 11 g Fib, 32 g Prot, 331 mg Calc.

FYI To finely crush the fennel, loosely wrap the seeds in a clean kitchen towel and pound with a rolling pin or a small heavy saucepan.

Lasagna Bolognese

Shrimp Scampi

LEVEL Basic

PREP 20 min

COOK/BROIL 10 min

SERVES 4

▲ 1 **pound large shrimp, peeled**

4 **teaspoons unsalted butter**

2 **shallots, minced**

1 **garlic clove, minced**

Juice of ½ lemon

½ **teaspoon salt**

Pinch red pepper flakes

2 **tablespoons chopped fresh parsley**

1. To butterfly shrimp, with small knife, cut along curved back of each shrimp almost, but not completely, through. With tip of knife, lift out dark vein. Open each shrimp and press down to slightly flatten.

2. Melt butter in large nonstick skillet over medium heat. Add shallots and garlic; cook, stirring, until shallots are golden, about 5 minutes. Remove skillet from heat; stir in lemon juice, salt, and pepper flakes. Add shrimp and toss to coat.

3. Preheat broiler. Arrange shrimp in single layer in shallow flameproof baking dish. Broil 5 inches from heat until lightly browned and just opaque in center, about 3 minutes per side. Serve sprinkled with parsley.

PER SERVING (6 SHRIMP): 115 grams, 133 Cal, 5 g Total Fat, 3 g Sat Fat, 0 g Trans Fat, 178 mg Chol, 487 mg Sod, 3 g Total Carb, 1 g Total Sugar, 0 g Fib, 19 g Prot, 45 mg Calc.

▲ **HEALTHY EXTRA** Enjoy these garlicky shrimp with a side of steamed whole green beans and brown rice (⅔ cup of cooked brown rice with each serving will increase the *PointsPlus* value by *3*).

Turkey-Vegetable Noodle Bowl

5 PointsPlus® value

Per Serving

LEVEL Basic

PREP 15 min

COOK 20 min

SERVES 6

¼ **pound multigrain linguine**

2 **garlic cloves, minced**

1½ **teaspoons grated peeled fresh ginger**

▲ 1 **pound turkey cutlets, cut into thin strips**

▲ 1 **(32-ounce) carton reduced-sodium chicken broth**

3 **tablespoons sake or dry sherry**

2 **tablespoons reduced-sodium soy sauce**

▲ ¼ **pound shiitake mushrooms, stemmed and caps sliced**

▲ 6 **scallions, sliced**

▲ 1 **carrot, thinly sliced**

¼ **cup lightly packed fresh cilantro leaves**

1. Cook linguine according to package directions, omitting salt if desired.

2. Meanwhile, spray nonstick Dutch oven with nonstick spray and set over medium-high heat. Add garlic and ginger; cook, stirring, until fragrant, about 30 seconds. Stir in turkey.

3. Add broth, sake, and soy sauce to turkey mixture; bring to boil. Reduce heat and simmer, covered, until turkey is cooked through, about 10 minutes. Stir in mushrooms, scallions, and carrot. Cook, covered, until vegetables are tender, about 5 minutes. Add linguine, tossing to mix well. Divide evenly among 6 soup bowls and sprinkle with cilantro.

PER SERVING (GENEROUS 1 CUP): 305 grams, 192 Cal, 1 g Total Fat, 0 g Sat Fat, 0 g Trans Fat, 30 mg Chol, 558 mg Sod, 21 g Total Carb, 3 g Total Sugar, 4 g Fib, 25 g Prot, 37 mg Calc

▲ **HEALTHY EXTRA** A bowl of edamame is a great way to whet your appetite for this dish (½ cup of cooked shelled edamame for each serving will increase the *PointsPlus* value by *2*).

Lean Protein

▶ **Make meat the side dish.** Instead of letting it take center stage, move a fist-size skinless chicken breast or piece of steak or lamb to a corner of your plate and fill the rest with veggies and salads. This strategy ensures that you get enough lean protein but not too much—and it keeps a meal's calories under control.

▶ **Try a new bird.** Don't get stuck in a chicken rut; treat your taste buds to Cornish game hen, duck, turkey, or capon. They're all easy to cook, affordable, and delicious hot or cold.

▶ **Take the alternative route.** Your protein intake doesn't have to consist entirely of meat, poultry, or fish. Go vegetarian a few meals a week, using tofu, tempeh, eggs, lentils, or beans as your primary protein source. Similarly, keep hard-cooked eggs in the fridge for a quick, protein-rich snack.

Salmon and Vegetable Teriyaki

6 PointsPlus® value
Per Serving

LEVEL Basic

PREP 20 min

COOK/BROIL 15 min

SERVES 4

⅓ **cup sake or dry sherry**

3 **tablespoons reduced-sodium soy sauce**

4 **(¼-pound) skinless salmon fillets**

2 **garlic cloves, minced**

2 **teaspoons grated peeled fresh ginger**

▲ 2 **different color bell peppers, thinly sliced**

▲ 1 **cup snow peas, trimmed and cut crosswise in half**

▲ 1 **carrot, cut into matchstick strips**

1. To make teriyaki sauce, bring sake and soy sauce to boil in small saucepan. Reduce heat and simmer until sauce is reduced to ¼ cup, about 5 minutes. Remove pan from heat.

2. Spray broiler rack with nonstick spray. Preheat broiler.

3. Place salmon on prepared broiler rack. Broil 5 inches from heat just until opaque in center, about 4 minutes per side, brushing with 2 tablespoons of sauce halfway through broiling time.

4. Meanwhile, spray large nonstick skillet with nonstick spray and set over medium-high heat. Add garlic and ginger; cook, stirring constantly, until fragrant, about 30 seconds. Add bell peppers, snow peas, and carrot; cook, stirring frequently, until vegetables are crisp-tender, about 4 minutes longer.

5. Drizzle vegetables with remaining 2 tablespoons sauce. Serve with salmon.

PER SERVING (1 SALMON FILLET WITH ½ CUP VEGETABLES): 226 grams, 250 Cal, 9 g Total Fat, 1 g Sat Fat, 0 g Trans Fat, 72 mg Chol, 363 mg Sod, 8 g Total Carb, 3 g Total Sugar, 2 g Fib, 28 g Prot, 37 mg Calc.

FYI **Double or triple the teriyaki sauce** and use the extra for broiled steaks, poultry, or vegetables. It will keep indefinitely in the refrigerator.

Vegetarian Soba Salad

Vegetarian Soba Salad

8
PointsPlus®
value

Per Serving

LEVEL Basic
PREP 15 min
COOK 20 min
SERVES 5

½ **pound soba noodles**

2 **tablespoons mirin or dry sherry**

1 **tablespoon rice vinegar**

1 **tablespoon reduced-sodium soy sauce**

1 **teaspoon Asian (dark) sesame oil**

1 **garlic clove, minced**

½ **teaspoon grated peeled fresh ginger**

▲ ¼ **pound sugar snap peas, trimmed and cut crosswise in half**

▲ 1 **(14-ounce) package extra-firm tofu, drained and cut into 1-inch cubes**

▲ 1 **red bell pepper, thinly sliced**

▲ 4 **scallions, thinly sliced**

1. Cook noodles according to package directions. With tongs, transfer noodles to colander; drain; reserving cooking liquid. Rinse noodles under cold running water; drain again. Transfer to large bowl.

2. To make dressing, whisk together mirin, vinegar, soy sauce, sesame oil, garlic, and ginger in small bowl.

3. Return cooking liquid to boil. Add sugar snap peas and boil just until bright green, about 2 minutes. Drain in colander. Rinse under cold running water; drain again.

4. Add tofu, bell pepper, scallions, and sugar snap peas to noodles in bowl. Drizzle with dressing and gently toss to coat. Serve at room temperature or refrigerate to serve chilled.

PER SERVING (ABOUT 1 CUP): 198 grams, 268 Cal, 6 g Total Fat, 0 g Sat Fat, 0 g Trans Fat, 0 mg Chol, 442 mg Sod, 42 g Total Carb, 4 g Total Sugar, 2 g Fib, 15 g Prot, 189 mg Calc.

▲ **HEALTHY EXTRA** End the meal with a fruit salad of fresh lychees, sliced kiwifruit, and halved strawberries.

Scallop and Bell Pepper Stir-Fry

LEVEL Basic

PREP 15 min

COOK 10 min

SERVES 4

▲ 1   **pound sea scallops**

   2   **garlic cloves, minced**

   1   **teaspoon grated peeled fresh ginger**

▲ ½   **pound asparagus, cut into 1 ½-inch lengths**

▲ 2   **different color bell peppers, thinly sliced**

▲ 1   **small onion, thinly sliced**

▲ 1   **carrot, cut into matchstick strips**

   2   **tablespoons dry sherry**

   1   **tablespoon reduced-sodium soy sauce**

▲ 2   **cups hot cooked brown rice**

1. Pat scallops dry with paper towels. Spray nonstick wok or large deep skillet with nonstick spray and set over high heat. Add scallops and stir-fry until browned but still slightly translucent in center, about 2 minutes. Transfer to plate; keep warm.

2. Spray wok with nonstick spray. Add garlic and ginger; stir-fry until fragrant, about 30 seconds. Add asparagus, bell peppers, onion, and carrot; stir-fry until vegetables are crisp-tender, about 4 minutes.

3. Stir in sherry and soy sauce; bring to boil. Boil, stirring, until flavors are blended, about 30 seconds. Return scallops to wok and stir-fry just until heated through, about 1 minute longer. Serve with rice.

PER SERVING (1¼ CUPS SCALLOP MIXTURE AND ½ CUP RICE): 346 grams, 310 Cal, 2 g Total Fat, 0 g Sat Fat, 0 g Trans Fat, 66 mg Chol, 517 mg Sod, 39 g Total Carb, 5 g Total Sugar, 5 g Fib, 32 g Prot, 80 mg Calc.

FYI If you see a white strip (muscle) along the short edge of a **scallop**, remove it before cooking. Although the muscle is edible, it's the toughest part of the scallop.

Tex-Mex Chef's Salad

LEVEL Basic

PREP 20 min

BAKE/COOK 20 min

SERVES 4

3 **(6-inch) corn tortillas, each cut into 8 wedges**

▲ 1 **red onion, chopped**

2 **garlic cloves, minced**

¾ **pound ground lean pork**

3 **tablespoons salt-free fajita seasoning**

¼ **cup water**

▲ ½ **cup canned reduced-sodium black beans, rinsed and drained**

▲ ½ **cup canned Mexican-style corn, drained**

¼ **cup chopped fresh cilantro**

▲ 3 **cups lightly packed baby spinach**

▲ 1 **tomato, diced**

1. Preheat oven to 400°F. Spray large nonstick baking sheet with nonstick spray.

2. Arrange tortillas on prepared baking sheet in single layer; lightly spray with nonstick spray. Bake tortillas, turning occasionally, until crisp and edges begin to curl slightly, about 10 minutes. Transfer baking sheet to rack and let cool completely.

3. Meanwhile, spray large nonstick skillet with nonstick spray and set over medium heat. Add onion and garlic; cook, stirring, until onion is golden, about 7 minutes. Add pork and fajita seasoning; cook, breaking pork apart with wooden spoon, until lightly browned, about 8 minutes. Stir in water. Increase heat to medium-high and cook, stirring occasionally, until water is evaporated, about 3 minutes. Add beans, corn, and cilantro; cook, stirring, until heated through, about 1 minute.

4. Line large platter with spinach. Top with pork mixture and tomato. Tuck tortilla chips into pork mixture.

PER SERVING (ABOUT ¾ CUP SPINACH, ¾ CUP PORK MIXTURE, AND 6 TORTILLA CHIPS):
230 grams, 249 Cal, 7 g Total Fat, 2 g Sat Fat, 0 g Trans Fat, 42 mg Chol, 249 mg Sod, 26 g Total Carb, 4 g Total Sugar, 4 g Fib, 20 g Prot, 47 mg Calc.

 FYI Give this salad a **dose of extra heat** by sprinkling the tortillas with chili powder before baking them in step 2.

Easy Chimichangas

LEVEL Basic
PREP 15 min
COOK/BAKE 35 min
SERVES 4

▲ ½ **pound ground lean beef (5% fat or less)**

▲ 1 **onion, finely chopped**

1 **garlic clove, minced**

2 **teaspoons chili powder**

1 **teaspoon dried oregano**

▲ 1 **(8-ounce) can no-salt added tomato sauce**

⅓ **cup shredded reduced-fat pepper Jack cheese**

4 **(8-inch) whole wheat flour tortillas, warmed**

1. Preheat oven to 400°F. Lightly spray nonstick baking sheet with nonstick spray.

2. To make filling, spray medium nonstick skillet with nonstick spray and set over medium-high heat. Add beef, onion, garlic, chili powder, and oregano; cook, breaking beef apart with wooden spoon, until browned, about 6 minutes. Stir in tomato sauce and bring to boil. Reduce heat and simmer until flavors are blended and mixture is slightly thickened, about 5 minutes. Remove skillet from heat and stir in pepper Jack.

3. Spoon about ½ cup of filling down center of each tortilla. Fold in sides and roll up to enclose filling. Place chimichangas, seam side down, on prepared baking sheet. Lightly spray tops with nonstick spray. Bake until crisp and golden, about 20 minutes.

PER SERVING (1 CHIMICHANGA): 191 grams, 283 Cal, 8 g Total Fat, 3 g Sat Fat, 0 g Trans Fat, 39 mg Chol, 300 mg Sod, 31 g Total Carb, 6 g Total Sugar, 4 g Fib, 19 g Prot, 164 mg Calc.

▲ **HEALTHY EXTRA** Serve the chimichangas topped with chopped fresh tomatoes, sliced scallions, and chopped fresh parsley.

Easy Chimichangas

Turkey Chili with Black Beans

6 PointsPlus value
Per Serving

LEVEL Basic
PREP 15 min
COOK 1 hr 25 min
SERVES 6

▲ 1   **large red onion, chopped**

▲ 1   **(4½-ounce) can chopped mild green chiles**

   3   **garlic cloves, minced**

   2   **tablespoons chili powder**

   2   **tablespoons salt-free Creole seasoning**

▲ 1   **pound ground skinless turkey breast**

▲ 2   **(14½-ounce) cans no-salt added diced tomatoes**

▲ 1   **cup fat-free salsa**

   ½   **cup water**

▲ 2   **(15½-ounce) cans reduced-sodium black beans, rinsed and drained**

1. Spray nonstick Dutch oven with nonstick spray and set over medium heat. Add onion and cook, stirring, until softened, about 5 minutes. Add chiles, garlic, chili powder, and Creole seasoning; cook, stirring, until fragrant, about 1 minute. Add turkey and cook, breaking it apart with wooden spoon, until browned about 8 minutes.

2. Stir tomatoes, salsa, and water into turkey mixture; bring to boil. Reduce heat and simmer, covered, until flavors are blended and chili is slightly thickened, about 1 hour. Stir in beans and cook until heated through, about 3 minutes longer.

PER SERVING (1⅓ CUPS): 465 grams, 230 Cal, 2 g Total Fat, 0 g Sat Fat, 0 g Trans Fat, 30 mg Chol, 602 mg Sod, 34 g Total Carb, 9 g Total Sugar, 10 g Fib, 26 g Prot, 82 mg Calc.

▲ **HEALTHY EXTRA** Serve this chili with shredded cheese (1 ounce of fat-free Cheddar cheese with each serving will increase the *PointsPlus* value by *1*).

Thai Steak Skewers

LEVEL Basic
PREP 25 min
GRILL 5 min
SERVES 4

▲ ¼ **cup finely chopped red onion**

2 **tablespoons honey**

1 **tablespoon finely chopped fresh lemongrass**

▲ 1 **jalapeño pepper, seeded and minced**

2 **garlic cloves, minced**

2 **teaspoons grated peeled fresh ginger**

2 **teaspoons reduced-sodium soy sauce**

2 **teaspoons Asian fish sauce**

1 **teaspoon Asian (dark) sesame oil**

▲ 1 **(1-pound) top round steak, trimmed and cut into ¼-inch slices**

▲ 2 **scallions, finely chopped**

2 **tablespoons finely chopped unsalted peanuts**

1. Combine onion, honey, lemongrass, jalapeño, garlic, ginger, soy sauce, fish sauce, and sesame oil in large zip-close plastic bag; add steak. Squeeze out air and seal bag; turn to coat steak. Refrigerate, turning bag occasionally, at least 1 hour or up to overnight.

2. Spray grill rack with nonstick spray. Preheat grill to medium-high or prepare medium-high fire using direct method.

3. Remove steak from marinade. Scrape off any excess marinade and discard. Thread steak onto 8 (8-inch) metal skewers. Place on grill rack and grill until beef is well marked, about 3 minutes per side for medium. Sprinkle with scallions and peanuts.

PER SERVING (2 SKEWERS): 131 grams, 242 Cal, 8 g Total Fat, 2 g Sat Fat, 0 g Trans Fat, 65 mg Chol, 335 mg Sod, 12 g Total Carb, 10 g Total Sugar, 1 g Fib, 29 g Prot, 22 mg Calc.

 FYI No fresh lemongrass on hand? Substitute the grated zest of 1 lemon.

Beef, Tomato, and Peanut Salad

4 PointsPlus value
Per Serving

LEVEL Basic

PREP 20 min

COOK None

SERVES 6

3 tablespoons lime juice

1 tablespoon brown sugar

2 teaspoons Asian fish sauce

½ teaspoon Thai red curry paste

▲ ¾ pound thinly sliced fat-free roast beef, cut into thin strips

▲ ½ small orange or yellow bell pepper, diced

▲ 2 plum tomatoes, chopped

▲ 1 small onion, thinly sliced

▲ 1 small cucumber, peeled, halved, and thinly sliced

¼ cup coarsely chopped fresh cilantro

¼ cup coarsely chopped fresh mint

▲ 6 large butter lettuce leaves

¼ cup unsalted peanuts, finely chopped

Lime wedges

1. To make dressing, whisk together lime juice, brown sugar, fish sauce, and curry paste in small bowl.

2. Toss together roast beef, bell pepper, tomato, onion, cucumber, cilantro, and mint in large bowl. Add dressing and toss to coat evenly.

3. Place lettuce on platter; top with roast beef mixture. Sprinkle evenly with peanuts and serve with lime wedges.

PER SERVING (⅙ OF SALAD): 167 grams, 141 Cal, 5 g Total Fat, 1 g Sat Fat, 0 g Trans Fat, 27 mg Chol, 744 mg Sod, 12 g Total Carb, 7 g Total Sugar, 2 g Fib, 14 g Prot, 28 mg Calc.

▲ **HEALTHY EXTRA** Add 1 carrot, grated, to the salad in step 2.

Chicken and Rice Salad

4 PointsPlus® value
Per Serving

LEVEL Basic
PREP 15 min
COOK 20 min
SERVES 6

▲ 1   **cup brown basmati rice**

3   **tablespoons chopped fresh mint**

Juice of 1 large lime

1   **tablespoon unseasoned rice vinegar**

2   **teaspoons Asian (dark) sesame oil**

¼   **teaspoon hot pepper sauce**

▲ 2   **cups lightly packed spinach, coarsely chopped**

▲ 1   **cup mung bean sprouts**

▲ ½   **small red onion, diced**

▲ ¾   **cup thinly sliced cooked skinless chicken breast**

1. Cook rice according to package directions; fluff with fork. Transfer to serving bowl and let cool completely.

2. Meanwhile, to make dressing, whisk together mint, lime juice, vinegar, sesame oil, and pepper sauce in small bowl.

3. Add spinach, bean sprouts, and onion to rice in bowl. Drizzle with half of dressing and toss to coat evenly. Top with chicken and drizzle with remaining dressing.

PER SERVING (1 CUP): 96 grams, 150 Cal, 2 g Total Fat, 0 g Sat Fat, 0 g Trans Fat, 15 mg Chol, 35 mg Sod, 27 g Total Carb, 2 g Total Sugar, 2 g Fib, 9 g Prot, 19 mg Calc.

FYI Crunchy with a hint of sweetness, mung bean sprouts are perfect for salads. Look for plump sprouts that are not stringy or discolored. Mung bean sprouts may be refrigerated in a zip-close plastic bag for up to 2 days.

Ginger Shrimp and Vegetables

Ginger Shrimp and Vegetables

LEVEL Basic
PREP 15 min
COOK 10 min
SERVES 4

2   teaspoons canola oil
▲ 1   pound peeled and deveined large shrimp
2   garlic cloves, minced
1½   teaspoons grated peeled fresh ginger
▲ 2   red bell peppers, thinly sliced
▲ 1   cup snow peas, trimmed and halved
▲ 1   carrot, shredded
2   tablespoons light (low-fat) coconut milk
2   teaspoons brown sugar
2   teaspoons reduced-sodium soy sauce
▲ 2   cups hot cooked brown rice

1. Heat nonstick wok or deep large nonstick skillet over medium-high heat until drop of water sizzles in pan; add 1 teaspoon of oil and swirl to coat pan. Add shrimp and stir-fry until just opaque in center, about 3 minutes. Transfer to plate; keep warm.

2. Heat remaining 1 teaspoon oil in wok. Add garlic and ginger; stir-fry until fragrant, about 30 seconds. Add bell peppers, snow peas, and carrot; stir-fry until vegetables are crisp-tender, about 3 minutes. Stir in coconut milk, brown sugar, and soy sauce; stir-fry until sugar is dissolved, about 30 seconds. Stir in shrimp and toss until heated through, about 1 minute longer. Serve with rice.

PER SERVING (ABOUT 1 CUP SHRIMP WITH VEGETABLES AND ½ CUP RICE): 291 grams, 267 Cal, 5 g Total Fat, 1 g Sat Fat, 0 g Trans Fat, 168 mg Chol, 274 mg Sod, 33 g Total Carb, 6 g Total Sugar, 4 g Fib, 22 g Prot, 64 mg Calc.

FYI When grating fresh ginger, for best results, use the small holes of a box grater. A ½-inch piece of ginger will yield about 1½ teaspoons of grated ginger.

Chunky Guacamole, page 140

Index

Dry and Liquid Measurement Equivalents

If you are converting the recipes in this book to metric measurements, use the following chart as a guide.

TEASPOONS	TABLESPOONS	CUPS	FLUID OUNCES
3 teaspoons	1 tablespoon		½ fluid ounce
6 teaspoons	2 tablespoons	⅛ cup	1 fluid ounce
8 teaspoons	2 tablespoons plus 2 teaspoons	⅙ cup	
12 teaspoons	4 tablespoons	¼ cup	2 fluid ounces
15 teaspoons	5 tablespoons	⅓ cup minus 1 teaspoon	
16 teaspoons	5 tablespoons plus 1 teaspoon	⅓ cup	
18 teaspoons	6 tablespoons	¼ cup plus 2 tablespoons	3 fluid ounces
24 teaspoons	8 tablespoons	½ cup	4 fluid ounces
30 teaspoons	10 tablespoons	½ cup plus 2 tablespoons	5 fluid ounces
32 teaspoons	10 tablespoons plus 2 teaspoons	⅔ cup	
36 teaspoons	12 tablespoons	¾ cup	6 fluid ounces
42 teaspoons	14 tablespoons	1 cup minus 2 tablespoons	7 fluid ounces
45 teaspoons	15 tablespoons	1 cup minus 1 tablespoon	
48 teaspoons	16 tablespoons	1 cup	8 fluid ounces

TEASPOONS	
¼ teaspoon	1 milliliter
½ teaspoon	2 milliliters
1 teaspoon	5 milliliters
1 tablespoon	15 milliliters
2 tablespoons	30 milliliters
3 tablespoons	45 milliliters
¼ cup	60 milliliters
⅓ cup	80 milliliters
½ cup	120 milliliters
⅔ cup	160 milliliters
¾ cup	175 milliliters
1 cup	240 milliliters
1 quart	950 milliliters

OVEN TEMPERATURE			
250°F	120°C	400°F	200°C
275°F	140°C	425°F	220°C
300°F	150°C	450°F	230°C
325°F	160°C	475°F	250°C
350°F	180°C	500°F	260°C
375°F	190°C	525°F	270°C

LENGTH	
1 inch	25 millimeters
1 inch	2.5 centimeters

WEIGHT	
1 ounce	30 grams
¼ pound	120 grams
½ pound	240 grams
1 pound	480 grams

Note: Measurement of less than ⅛ teaspoon is considered a dash or a pinch. Metric volume measurements are approximate.